Your Ministry
Of Prayer

Lay Action Ministry Program, Inc.
5827 S. Rapp Street
Littleton, CO 80120

David C. Cook Publishing Co.
850 N. Grove Avenue
Elgin, IL 60120

Scripture quotations, unless otherwise noted, are taken from the *Holy Bible: New International
Version*, ©1978, 1984 International Bible Society, used by permission of Zondervan Bible
Publishers.

David C. Cook Publishing Co.
850 North Grove Avenue
Elgin, IL 60120
Printed in U.S.A.

Editor: Becky Dodson
Designer: Chris Patchel
Cover: Lois Rosio Sprague

ISBN: 0-89191-490-0
Library of Congress Catalog Number: 89-81111

TABLE OF CONTENTS

LAY ACTION
MINISTRY PROGRAM

LAMP Courses are based on the HEAD, HEART, and HANDS approach to learning. HEAD represents Bible content that you want to know. HEART represents your personal application of the truth. HANDS refers to the LAMP goal of preparing you to *use course content in the lives of other people*—imparting to others what you have learned (see II Tim. 2:2).

Your Ministry of Prayer can be a life-changing experience for you. First, you will carefully work through each lesson in your own private study. Then you will discuss each lesson with other members of your group. Finally, you will be encouraged to apply the principles in ministry to your church and community.

Course Requirements

This course is for every Christian who is willing to put forth the effort in personal study. But we want you to know "up front" that *it is going to cost you a good hour of home study for each lesson*. Make every effort to spend this much time as a minimum requirement. Also, in order to maximize your personal study time during the week, faithful attendance at the group meetings should be considered a high priority. Not only will you benefit from this group interaction, but the others attending will undoubtedly gain as well.

D. the lesson early in the week (by end of ↓Fed.) then review it + mull it over 'til next meeting.

How to Use This Course

Though you may complete the course by yourself, you will normally be preparing for a weekly group meeting. In this meeting you will be an active participant because of your personal study. One lesson is to be completed each week, prior to coming to the weekly group meeting.

The weekly group meeting for this course features a discussion of the lesson that you have studied during the week. It also includes other elements to encourage group life, and to guide group members toward personal application of the material. The meeting, planned for at least a full hour, should be led by a person who enjoys leading discussions and helping people learn. The leader will study the lesson in the same way as anyone else in the group. In addition to the Lesson Plans at the back of this book, a **Leader's Guide** provides fuller, more detailed suggestions for conducting each weekly group meeting. A Leader's Guide can be obtained from:

LAY ACTION MINISTRY PROGRAM, INC.
5827 SOUTH RAPP STREET
LITTLETON, CO 80120
(303) 730-8340

or:
DAVID C. COOK PUBLISHING CO.
850 NORTH GROVE AVENUE
ELGIN, IL 60120

PRAYER:
KEY TO KINGDOM
BUILDING

The "big picture"

The great preacher Charles Spurgeon was once asked about the secret of his successful preaching ministry by which countless seekers were won to Christ. Spurgeon's response was to show the questioner a basement under the sanctuary where, every Sunday morning during the preaching, hundreds of "prayer warriors" lifted their hands and hearts to God on His behalf.

Spurgeon was apparently aware of the crucial importance of such a "behind the scenes" ministry. Perhaps you, too, have had a feeling that the work of God's Kingdom cannot be done with merely human resources. There must be people dedicated to prayer—and you want to be one of them. In response to your desire, consider God's words to you: "Call to me and I will answer you and tell you great and unsearchable things you do not know" (Jer. 33:3).

In this first lesson, let's take a look at the vast behind the scenes Kingdom where God's work and will are carried out. By getting a good glimpse of that Kingdom before jumping into all we have to learn about the ministry of prayer, we will be reminded of our vital importance to the ongoing execution of God's work in the world. Because in the clash of kingdoms, prayer is the means of accomplishing God's will. Thus, to learn to pray, *really* pray, is an adventure, and you are invited to join in the expedition!

We'll begin by focusing on the Kingdom at three different levels: the big picture of God's reign in the world, the local church in its front-line engagement with the kingdoms of this world, and the individual believer whose life and prayers fit into this scenario of God's great plan for the ages.

God's Reign in the World

X What, exactly, *is* the Kingdom in its broadest sense? First, it is *the arena of Christ's influence in the world.* Wherever Jesus Christ is loved and worshiped, there is the Kingdom of God. That means that all who are indwelt with God's Spirit, around the world, are included in the Kingdom. Wherever His Spirit is at work in the world, even among unbelievers, there, too, the Kingdom of God is making its impact.

The Kingdom is both present as well as potential. That is, the Kingdom is yet to be revealed in its fullness at the culmination of this age. For more insight into this "yet/not yet" character of the Kingdom, look at the following Bible passages, and record your insights:

Matthew 4:17—5:20. In what ways did the coming of Jesus and the beginning of His earthly ministry usher in God's Kingdom more fully?

1. (4:17) Brought people into a relationship w/ God.
2. (4:19) Called them to a life-commitment to Gods kingdom miss
3. (5:3-12) Raised the standards for kingdom participants
4. (5:13-16) Showed the primary function redeemed fill
5. (5:17-20) Objective of kingdom - Righteousness.

Romans 8:18-25. What is the ultimate goal of God's work in the world?

Display of His glory. Freedom
Restoration of earth

8

What evidence of longing (or "groaning") for the Kingdom to be revealed do you have within yourself? What evidence do you see in the lives of your friends and/or neighbors?

Ache to be free of sin. So do others.
Despair of hopelessness. Long for Justice.

In what ways do you see the Kingdom of God at work in the world today and in your own community?

Global

National

Community

Work, Home, Team Life

What would you consider to be the greatest challenge to the spread of the Kingdom in the world today?

Jn 14:12-14

It is through the ministry of prayer & its fruit that the influence of the Kingdom of God is felt in my world. Therefore the greatest challenge is to pray.

(priority)

Jesus, in one of His conversations with His commissioned workers, gives us an amazing insight into the impact our lives can make upon the advance of the Kingdom. Take a couple of minutes to read Luke 10:1-18. The 72 disciples had just returned from a mission of Kingdom preaching and good works. In verse 17 they tell Jesus of their great success against all spiritual opposition. But Jesus' immediate comment (vs. 18) shows that these disciples had only a dim idea of just how great their accomplishments in the Kingdom really were.

Looking at the disciples' report in verse 17, what do you

(Pos) God won big.

think Jesus meant by His statement in verse 18?

(Neg) Satan's effectiveness ~~removed~~ *restricted*. His authority replaced.
His influence removed.

Jesus gave the disciples a glimpse of the big picture. They had gone about their duties in the world of things that they could see and touch. They had walked on dusty roads, visited the towns and marketplaces and homes of real people, touched real bodies for healing, and preached the Good News of God's salvation. And all of that had been a success. But if they could only have seen it from Jesus' perspective. Jesus had seen Satan falling as a result of their obedient efforts!

According to Luke 10:2, what is our responsibility in regard to the supply of workers?

Pray for them

What indication is there in verse 3 that our prayers should not end once these workers have been sent out?

Battles are in store
for those who go out.

What happens in the Kingdom when we pray? In many cases we will have no idea of the impact our prayers have had upon the spiritual "battles" that take place on the front lines between God's Kingdom and the kingdoms of this world. Are you beginning to get a sense of the enormous implications of being a Kingdom person? All aspects of our daily lives, our actions, words, deeds, *and especially our prayers,* have a profound impact upon the progress of God's Kingdom on earth. But how, specifically, can we make a difference?

Prayer in the Church

Take a look at two important passages that show us how the early church made headway in spreading the Kingdom: Acts 2:42-47 and 6:1-7.

10

a steadfast + singleminded commitment to a certain course of action

voted to:

According to the first passage, what were the top priorities for the early Christians in their church life?

1. _Discipleship_
2. _Fellowship   Worship_
3. _Prayer_
4. _Evangelism_

According to the second passage, what were the two main priorities in the minds of the church leaders at that time?

Prayer + Ministry of Word

Based on verse 7, how "successful" was the church in those days?

Acts 2 — winsome testimony   Acts 6 Word
Conversions   spread; Disciples
multi-
plied

What do you think would happen in the Church today if more attention were given to the ministry of prayer? Share your vision:

I think God would be more free
to work in our midst. Powerful Victories!

Local churches are the corporate units that make up the Kingdom. They are called by God to live as (what author Howard Snyder has called) the community of the King. The life, works, and relationships of each local church should, in a sense, show the world what life in the heavenly Kingdom is like—an island in the sea of humanity that lives in peace, love, and good will, proclaiming the message of God's grace. Is your church an example of Heaven on earth?

Naturally, every local church has its flaws and shortcomings since it is made up of mere human beings with problems and sins. Those things are still being dealt with by the Holy Spirit within each member. But don't let these shortcomings dim your vision of the local church's role in spreading the Kingdom's influence.

In the New Testament period, the apostle Paul was powerfully used in the extending of God's kingdom.Carefully study II Corinthians 2:14-16. From this passage, what is your initial impression of the Church's importance in the world? Explain.

_____

_____

_____

_____

According to the notes in the *NIV Study Bible:* "The imagery [of triumphal procession] is that of a Roman triumph in which the victorious general would lead his soldiers and the captives they had taken in festive procession, while the people watched and applauded and the air was filled with the sweet smell released by the burning of spices in the streets. So the Christian, called to spiritual warfare, is triumphantly led by God in Christ, and it is through him that God spreads everywhere the 'fragrance' of the knowledge of Christ."

We are the aroma of Christ in the world. Like the fragrance of flowers crushed under the feet of triumphant soldiers—announcing "Victory has been won!"—so we are the fragrance of a triumphant Christ who won salvation for us by His death and resurrection. Share how it makes you feel to know that you and those in your church group are constantly giving off the aroma of Christ to those around you:

_____

_____

_____

_____

In your opinion, what is the relationship between one's life-style and the effectiveness of his or her witness?

If you don't smell sweet you won't be attractive.

How have you noticed this relationship in your own life?

Do you have a sense of needing/wanting a more effective prayer life because of these great truths? Why?

Prayer and the Believer

So far we have talked about the big picture of the Kingdom, and we have looked at how the local church fits into that picture. Now lets focus on how you and I, within the local church, are such important parts of God's Kingdom mission in the world. Consider one more Biblical example that can help challenge us with the crucial need for people who are aware of what happens behind the scenes—people who want to be a part of the prayer ministry that can take place there.

Turn to Exodus 17:8-16 and read about Moses' incredible ministry on behalf of God's people. What was the significance of Moses' uplifted hands? (See vs. 15.)

Represents the ministry of prayer.

In your opinion, how important was Moses to the outcome of the battle?

He was the Key to victory.

What implications can you draw from this passage about the importance of people behind the scenes whose "hands [are] lifted up to the throne of the Lord"? (vs. 16)

There needs to be several.

They need to support one another.

Persevere; Creative; Confidence of effectiveness

Its important

During the remainder of this week before your group meeting for lesson one, try an experiment. Write the following phrase on a note card and carry it with you during the entire week: *"The Kingdom is here, and I can make a difference."* Ask God to remind you to take the card out periodically during the day and repeat the phrase, and pray a prayer of petition: "Lord, move me into a ministry of prayer." For your group meeting, be prepared to share how this effort at an inner consciousness of your role in the Kingdom and your vital ministry of prayer affected your life this past week. In what ways were your words, actions, and prayers affected by a broader perspective of your place in God's work in the world? Jot down some notes here during the week:

_____

_____

_____

Welcome to Your Ministry of Prayer

The real goal of this course is that—over the next several weeks—you will become challenged with the vital *ministry* of prayer. In fact, we hope that you will sense God's call to become a prayer minister. This means that you will commit yourself, with God's help, to praying for the needs of your church, your community, your nation, and for the needs of your church's missionaries around the world. Our prayers are a vital means through which God carries out His will.

In order to help you become an effective prayer minister and encourage the growth of your prayer ministry group, consider taking the following steps:

1. Develop a personal prayer notebook. Before coming to your group meeting next week, obtain a notebook with filler paper. LAMP suggests using a three-ring binder, either 5x8 or 6x9. Beginning next week, you will be shown how to organize and use your prayer notebook.

2. At some time in the next few weeks, select a person who will communicate current prayer requests weekly to each prayer minister. This person will be called the Prayer Ministers Coordinator.

3. Your pastor will need to get involved, too. He is needed to help provide prayer information to the prayer coordinator. If you have a church computer, these requests should be put there, where updates and printouts can be done with ease.

LAMP suggests that *Your Ministry of Prayer* be taught at least once each year, to recruit additional people to join your group of prayer ministers.

2

GEARING UP FOR A PRAYER MINISTRY

Chris, a mature Christian, is helping his friend Sal learn some things about praying. Let's listen in.

Sal: Prayer is soul food, eh?

Chris: Exactly. Believe me, it's practical.

Sal: I believe you, but I still can't seem to find time for it.

Chris: You'll never find time to pray.... You have to make time to pray. It takes sacrifice. Something has to go, usually something that seems important. . . . There's always some work that needs to be done. You just have to say no to it, sacrifice it, for the "one thing necessary."

I need to sacrifice non-essentials not essentials.

Sal: I see. It takes effort to start, then.

Chris: It sure does. It takes a deliberate, conscious effort of will. And there's no gimmick for that, no method, no "how." The first step is just deciding to do it. Not just *wishing,* but *deciding, willing.* If you really decide to do it, you'll do it. If you don't end up doing it, that means you didn't really decide to do it.
—From Peter Kreeft, *Prayer: The Great Conversation* (Servant Books)

Three Practical Matters

Someone has said that the most essential thing about prayer is not necessarily *how* you do it, but *whether* you do

it. Like merely reading a cookbook—rather than cook-
ing—we may learn quite a bit about praying without
actually doing it. Then spiritual starvation sets in.

But once we actually make the commitment to a ministry of prayer, we will need to focus on three practical
matters regarding the way we actually go about praying:
when, where, and how.

THE WHEN. Beginning with this course, LAMP suggests
that you commit to a prayer time everyday—of say 10 to
15 minutes, and more time after completing this course.

Since our lives often seem too full already, where are we
going to carve out this additional time for this very important ministry? Yet, how much of our feeble praying is
really due to a lack of time rather than a lack of desire? The
bottom line is: if we really want to do it—if we really
believe in this vital ministry and commit ourselves to it,
with the Lord's help we *will* find time for adequate praying.

In order to find time for prayer, J. O. Sanders makes the
practical suggestion that we "plug the leaks." Leaks? At
first blush you might not be able to think of any "leaks" in
your time management. But think through your day right
now. Look for less important parts—such as watching TV,
reading the daily paper, talking on the telephone, doing
household chores, etc. Estimate the time you spend on
these activities, then write down the amount of time you
feel you could reasonably save in each of these areas.

_TV_

Woodshop

_____

_____

We should not think of our day in terms only of hours, but in
smaller portions of time, and aim to make constructive use of

each of these. Dr. F. B. Meyer, noted preacher and author, packed more into his life than most of his contemporaries. And his secret? It was said of him that, like John Wesley, he divided his life into periods of five minutes and then endeavored to make each period count for God.

—J. O. Sanders, *Prayer Power Unlimited* (Chicago: Moody, 1977, 1984)

What does Ephesians 5:15, 16 say to you in this regard?

Make the most of our time. Accomplish spiritual & eternal tasks.

Applying the lesson of the minas (an ancient money unit) in Luke 19:11-27, what lesson in time management does this provide? *Involved in God's Kingdom work.*

We are accountable to God to invest the resource of our time for a spiritual return.

Write out your "action plan" for plugging the leaks, thus making time available for your ministry of prayer.

Shut myself in bedroom every night @ 5:10 on so. Spend 10 minutes each morning in prayer.

To effect such a radical change in our life-style will call for strength of will and a radical dependence on the power of God's Spirit.

THE WHERE. In one sense, you can pray anywhere, at any time, simply by shifting your inner attitude so that it focuses upon God's presence with you. I find myself praying this way throughout the day, and you probably do, too. But when it comes to the discipline of a regular prayer ministry, we will need to really *focus* on what we are doing. That could mean choosing a special, definite place for opening your heart to God. It should be a place of solitude, if possible, free from interruptions and distractions.

Perhaps the best reason for having a solitary place for prayer is that it follows the practice of Jesus Himself. What do we see about Jesus' practice in Matthew 14:23, Mark 1:35, and Luke 5:16?

He made the time, went to a chosen place where He wouldn't be interrupted.

Probably Jesus had many places where He could pray alone and without being disturbed.

What did He teach about the place for prayer in Matthew 6:6? Why? *— No destractions*

Praying in private. Guard against pretense in prayer. (For show)

There is a very practical reason for this advice. Many college students have found it helpful to designate the dormitory desk as a place for *study only*. The student will not eat at the desk, watch TV from the desk, sleep at the desk. It is the place for study. Thus, when that student sits down at the desk, her subconscious mind gears her whole body for the study task at hand. In the same way, when you come to your special place for prayer—and you know that is what you have come to do—you find your mind, body, spirit, and senses already positioning themselves for prayer through mere force of habit.

What are your thoughts about the best place for you to have a regular prayer time? List some of the options below, and put a star next to your first choice:

Basement

Upstairs school/Computer room

★ *Bedroom*

THE HOW. As you launch yourself into a regular prayer ministry, consider three suggestions which may help.

(First,) pray *conversationally* — as you would to another person. The Scriptures tell us that we have a personal God, one who is close to us, who cares about our every concern. We also know that, as Christians, we have become beloved children of the Heavenly Father. Thus, we have every encouragement to approach God honestly, with our lives transparent before Him.

(Second,) pray *specifically.* How often we pray in such general terms, that even if God *did* answer our prayer, we would never even know it! While we do not presume to dictate to God how He should answer our prayers, surely it must be part of God's pleasure to answer specific prayers in ways that cause us to be moved to praise. If you have small children, you know that they do not simply ask to be "blessed." They ask for food, drinks of water, bubble gum, candy, toys, books, etc.

How is this principle brought out in James 4:2, 3?

Some good things are withheld b/c we didn't pray.

(Third,) pray in an *organized* way. Prayer should be a way of life, as we invite God into our concerns throughout the day. In this way we find we are "praying without ceasing." But for the special ministry of prayer you will want to approach the task with specific purposes in mind.

One of the most popular ways of "organizing" a prayer ministry is to use the A-C-T-S method. The acrostic can help you remember to spend at least some of your prayer time each day in Adoration, Confession, Thanksgiving, and Supplication.

Take 15 minutes before going on in this lesson for a time alone with God. Before actually praying, think through the A-C-T-S formula and jot down the things that come to your mind. This may seem at first to be a kind of dry, dull "formula." But eventually, the A-C-T-S steps will all meld together to form a beautiful mosaic of fellowship time with God. Here's the space to write down some of the grist for your prayer mill:

Expressions of adoration that come to me:

God, your glory is awesome. You are worthy of all honor, praise, and glory because of Who you are and what you do.

Things I need to confess:

Lord I confess my on-again, off-again trust in you to raise up in our church a ministry that really changes lives & brings people to Christ.

Things for which I am thankful:

I am thankful that I am your child, I am thankful for my wife & boys. I am thankful for my friends and your calling upon my life here in Brazil.

People and needs that I want to bring before God:

My fellow learners in this men's prayer group. That we would become victorious & strong for You, our families, our church & the lost world.

Setting Up Your Prayer Notebook

Your prayer notebook should contain two main divisions, which we will call journaling and the prayer requests.

JOURNALING SECTION. I have a poster on my wall depicting a beautiful beach scene. The caption on the poster reads: "When I look, let me truly see." The poster reminds me to try not to let any of my life just slip by for want of attention. There is too much to really *experience* every day (both good and bad) if I will only stop to become fully aware and engaged with my environment. This is where the practice of journaling can be a tremendous help.

What is journaling? It is keeping a daily record of your journey through life with God. It is like keeping love letters—the entries becoming a record of God's love for you as you grow in Christ.

Now for some of the mechanics of the prayer notebook itself:

Buy a permanent notebook, either bound or with a ring binder. I use a 5x8 bound composition book with a hard cover. This book-like quality gives me a sense of the sacredness and permanence of what I write, rather than thinking of the journal as bits of paper clipped together. A three-ring binder is also an excellent choice, especially if it is compatible in size with your Bible.

Some people divide the journal into two or more parts. My own practice is to make a running account of daily entries in the first part of the book, with the second part consisting of an "expandable" prayer list. In part 1, the daily entries, I include my insights from Scripture, my thoughts about my Christian growth, written prayers, quotes from reading that I value. In short, the entries show a running dialogue with myself, God, and my concerns for others.

Don't worry about spelling, punctuation, grammar, or neatness when you write, since the journal is for you— unless you choose to read parts to others. So if you tend to scribble or use your own personal shorthand, so much the better. Keep your journal in a safe, private place.

Begin now to record your walk with God, your spiritual

22

journey. As author Morton Kelsey put it: "If God is truly the divine lover, then a day lived without a record of that relationship is a day which is less than full and whole."

PRAYER REQUESTS SECTION. The second part of your notebook is a record of specific prayer concerns and answers to prayer. You may organize this list in a variety of ways. Some people write down a simple list of requests. Others choose to organize their requests by topics—such as family, friends, relatives, local church, missions, etc. Still others list their requests by days: certain requests are prayed for on Mondays, others on Tuesdays, etc. Or you may want to list requests that you pray for daily, and others that you pray for less often—such as weekly.

Be sure to leave space for recording answers to prayer because: 1) it encourages you as you see that God is indeed answering prayer, and 2) it gives you additional reasons to praise Him.

Your Ministry of Prayer

So far in this course we've discussed some commitments you will need to make in order to get involved in a consistent ministry of prayer. Let's recap them:

• Hopefully you have already purchased a prayer notebook—either a bound book, or preferably a three-ring binder. If you don't have a notebook yet, be sure to obtain one soon.

• Organize the notebook into two parts—a journaling/ Scripture reading section in which you record your walk with God and your interaction with His Word, and the prayer section in which you will record specific requests for prayer.

• Determine the specific time that you plan to spend daily in prayer.

I want to spend *30 minutes* in prayer daily during the

weeks of this course on prayer. After completing the course I hope to spend _____.

Your assignment this week is to write out your list of requests that you want to pray for daily. The "Daily Prayer Requests" found on page 118 of this workbook is suggested. *Make every effort to complete your prayer commitment each day this week.*

During your group session this week, discuss who would be the right person to serve as your Prayer Ministers Coordinator. Have one of your group members talk with your pastor to get additional suggestions about who might be interested in this ministry. Just so you can begin thinking and praying about it, here is a list of the responsibilities of the Prayer Ministers Coordinator:

1. Ask your pastor to provide you with a weekly list of prayer requests from your church. Arrange to have this list typed each week by your church secretary, or make other satisfactory arrangements for typing.

2. Contact all missionaries and other outreach ministries of your church. Inform them that this Ministers of Prayer ministry is beginning and request that the church (or you directly) receive copies of their letters for prayer request information.

3. Establish this same arrangement with your denomination (or church fellowship group), as well as with at least one agency that has a Christian ministry on a national or governmental level.

4. Read through all information received and highlight requests for prayer.

5. Give this information to your church secretary (after proper arrangements have been made with your pastor) for typing.

6. Make copies of this prayer list each week, and distribute them to each of the Prayer Ministers.

This is a sizable responsibility—yet critical for the advancement of God's Kingdom in your community. If the responsibilities seem like too much for one person, consider dividing the tasks among two or more people. One person could just handle letters for missionaries; another just prayer requests from your church, leaving a third person to be the over-all Coordinator.

You are making important decisions this week. But please remember that, on one level, these really aren't *your* decisions, or *your* work at all. Recognize that God has been calling you to a life of prayer, and His Spirit provides the motivation and the power for you to carry it through (read Phil. 2:13 right now). All praise, honor, and glory to HIM!

3

THE GOD
OF OUR PRAYERS

C. S. Lewis said: "The prayer preceding all prayers is, 'May it be the real I who speaks. May it be the real Thou that I speak to.' " All of us have a God-image—a sense of what God is like in relation to us. This image develops early and can be influenced by a wide range of experiences, both good and bad—including those that may come from our own fathers. And, though you may know plenty of Scripture, your deep sense of who God really is can thus be somewhat distorted. The way you live and how you feel about yourself as you pray has a lot to do with your deeply ingrained sense of what God is like, and what His attitude toward you is.

Make some personal notes about the images or impressions of God that you find yourself holding in your mind during prayer, or at other times.

When I pray I sense a God sitting in a chair across from me. Leaning toward me, fastened on each word I speak. Ready to act, energize, bless.

The basic intent of this chapter is to give you a clearer Biblical picture of who God is. The assumption is that the better you know God, the better you can communicate with Him in prayer.

What information do we have regarding the kind of

God we talk to when we pray? What does it mean to pray to the "true" God as opposed to a distorted God-image that we may have developed in our minds? In this lesson you will take a closer look at these questions by reviewing the names of God in Scripture, and by surveying some of God's self-revealed attributes. Finally, you will take some time to face the image of God that you hold in your mind when you pray—to see how well that image reflects the God revealed to us in Scripture.

It is difficult to communicate with someone you don't know anything about. Thankfully, we have "feedback" about God from two areas: the physical world around us (read Ps. 19; Acts 14:17; Rom. 1:18-32; 2:9-16; 10:18); and, most importantly, Scripture. In this lesson we will focus on what the Bible teaches us about God in those areas that especially relate to our praying.

Names of God

We can quicken our awareness of the importance of this study through the following excerpt from *The New Bible Dictionary* (Eerdmans), p. 478, 861:

> A study of the word "name" in the Old Testament reveals how much this word means in Hebrew. The name is no mere label, but is significant of the real personality of him to who it belongs. It may derive from the circumstances of his birth (Gen. 5:29), or reflect his character (Gen. 27:36), and when a person puts his "name" upon a thing or another person the latter comes under his influence and protection . . . .
>
> We have only to consider how particular God was to name chosen individuals (eg., Gen. 17:5, 15, 19; Isa. 45:3, 4; Mt. 1:21), and how solemnly He revealed the meaning of His own name, and used it (Ex. 3:13-15; 33:19; 34:5, 6) to realize that the concept of "name" is both deep and clearly conceived . . . .

In the Old Testament, first written in Hebrew, God has revealed Himself through three major names:

1. EL has been translated "might," "strong," "Strong One," "prominent," and "strength." (See Num. 23:22; —EL Deut. 10:17; Isa. 9:6-7.) The much more frequent plural form, Elohim (EL–lo–heem)—used some 2,500 times—signifies the strong, covenant-keeping God who creates and is faithful to His creation.

Several compounds are also found with the name EL.

El Elyon (EL el–YON) means literally, "God, the Highest God." This designates God as the sovereign ruler of all the universe. What circumstance evokes this name of God in the following passages:

Genesis 14:20 _Victory in battle + deliverance of God's people_

Psalm 78:35 _Sovereign in the extending of just compassion._

Daniel 4:34 _God's demonstration that He is sovereign over the lives of people & Nations_

El Shaddai (EL shad–DAI) speaks of the all-sufficiency of God. It is likely derived from the Hebrew word for a woman's breast. Thus, God is the One who is mighty to nourish, satisfy, and supply. (See Gen. 17:1, 2; 28:3.)

Reflect on these "EL" names for God. Write down your thoughts which strengthen your desire to worship God or increase your confidence in prayer.

God's personal covenant to care for His people. God cares for us in our marriage + family life.

2. *ADONAI* (a–do–NAI) is translated "Lord," (with small letters) and means "Master," or "Owner." It indicates the truth that God is the owner of each member of the human family, and that He consequently claims the unre-

stricted obedience of all. At the same time, we claim our
right to His protection, provision, enablement, and direction. (See II Sam. 7:8-22; Ps. 8; 97:5; Isa. 6:1; Jer. 1:6.)

What feelings or attitude in calling God *Adonai* can you
express from your own heart?

He is master me are Servant
Your are master of all

3. *YAHWEH* (YAH–way). This is the name most frequently employed for God, being used some 6,828 times.
It is usually translated "LORD" (with small caps). The name
is derived from the Hebrew verb *havah*, "to be," or "being."
Thus, *Yahweh* (also pronounced Jehovah), is the Being who
is absolutely self-existent, the One who in Himself possesses essential life, permanent existence. He is the Uncaused Cause, the great I AM who always exists, eternal
and unchangeable.

English "
LORD "
Adonai
"GOD "

Several compound names of *Yahweh* in the Old Testament pointed toward, and were fulfilled by Christ.

Yahweh-tsidkenu (YAH-way tsid-KAY-noo) means "The
Lord our Righteousness." To what, or to whom does this
name refer in Jeremiah 23:6; 33:16?

He make Israel righteous
Salvation

The practical outworking of this name both for my life
and for my prayer ministry is: (See also II Cor. 5:21; I Jn.
2:29.)

unchangeable, dependable

He will share His righteousness
w/me. I should like it to reflect

Yahweh–shalom (YAH–way shal–LOHM) means "The
Lord is Peace." This name was used by Gideon after "the
angel of the Lord" spoke with him. Look at this passage in
Judges 6 now. Why did Gideon name the altar "the Lord
is Peace" in verses 23, 24?

Peace given b/c safety
provided

How was this peace brought about historically? (Isa. 53:5; Col. 1:19, 20)

_____

_____

The practical outworking of this name for my life and prayer ministry is: (See also Rom. 5:1, 2.)

God is always on my side

_____

Yahweh–shammah (YAH–way SHAM–mah) means "The Lord is There," Ezekiel 48:35. Imagine, the very presence of God among His people! How do the following passages give you comfort: Genesis 28:15; Exodus 33:14; Deuteronomy 20:1; Isaiah 43:2?

God never leave us

won't back off His promises

The practical outworking of this name for my life and prayer ministry is: (See also Mt. 28:20 and I Cor. 3:16.)

_____

_____

Yahweh–jireh (YAH–way yeer–EH) means "The Lord Shall See" or simply, "The Lord Provides." This name expresses Abraham's praise for what great provision? (Gen. 22, especially vs. 14)

_____

How was Abraham's faith expressed? (vss. 5 and 8)

_____

How does Paul apply this principle in Romans 8:32?

_____

Personal application: _____

_____

Yahweh-nissi (YAH-way nis-SEE) means "The Lord My Banner." See Exodus 17:15, where God gives Joshua and his army victory as Moses' hands were lifted in prayer. *Nissi*, translated variously as "pole," "ensign," "standard," stands for God's cause, His battle. It is a sign of deliverance and victory. The lesson about prayer for me is (compare Eph. 6:10-18):

_____

_____

Attributes of God

Biblical scholars through the years have been able to describe aspects of God's character, based upon what God says and does in the Scriptures, and upon what we can know of the Creator through His Creation (for example, see A.W. Tozer's book *Knowledge of the Holy*). Reflect on the list below. It will give you an idea of the traditional ways we have come to describe what we know of our great God:

Transcendent—"above and beyond" our understanding
Immanent—close to us; dwells within His Creation
Immutable—unchanging
Infinite—without beginning or end; limitless
Omniscient—possesses all knowledge
Omnipresent—always, everywhere present
Omnipotent—all-powerful
Loving—self-giving toward His creatures
Self-sufficient—doesn't need anything to be fulfilled
Faithful—keeps His Word and promises
Sovereign—in complete control, able to carry out His will
Good—has our best interests at heart
Just—always fair
Merciful—tempers justice with understanding and compassion
Long-suffering—patient with our short-comings

Can you name others?

_____

_____

Pick out three of these attributes that make the most impact on you personally. Tell why. How would it affect the way you pray if you were more continuously aware of that particular attribute of God?

● Attribute: _____

Why it makes impact: _____

_____

Affect on the way I pray: _____

_____

● Attribute: _____

Why it makes impact: _____

_____

Affect on the way I pray: _____

_____

● Attribute: _____

Why it makes impact: _____

_____

Affect on the way I pray: _____

_____

Now I'll share with you the three attributes that I chose: *Omniscience*: God knows all. (See Job 23:10; Ps. 139:1-16; Mt. 6:5-8; Heb. 4:13-16.) In my experience, there are few things worse than being misunderstood. What a relief not to have to "explain" to God—anything—in prayer. We are instantly, fully known. He knows us in a deep communion that transcends any level of intimacy or sharing we might approach with another human being. Someone has said that God does not just hear our prayers, He hears our whole life.

There is a real sense of relief in this for me. If God knows me through and through, yet still loves me, what could I tell Him that could possibly change His feelings toward me? Nothing! Thus, I am invited in complete honesty and openness, to tell Him everything.

Sovereignty: God is in control. (See I Chron. 29:11, 12; Jn. 10:29; 19:11; Rom. 9:19; Rev. 4:11.) A few years ago, when President Reagan was wounded by a gunman, the people of the United States saw Secretary of State Alexander Haig in a TV press conference say: "I am in charge here." But his voice was shaky, and his persona at that moment did not inspire confidence. Suppose we had a God who was trying hard to be in charge, but wasn't quite pulling it off? In a sense, the truth of God's sovereignty is the only thing that makes God worth praying to.

For me, the implication for prayer is crucial: God's will *shall* be done. Here is the prime motivation for our overriding attitude: "Thy will be done." Knowing that God is in control moves me to grow in my relationship with God, that I might more and more pray according to His perspective (His will)—since those are the prayers that are answered. (And, because God is sovereign, and not me, I can be thankful for the many times my prayers have *not* been answered the way I wanted.)

Goodness: God has my best at heart. (See Ps. 37:4; Jn. 10:10.) "Suppose I choose to live a life of faith (which will involve plenty of 'risky' decisions along the way), and I thereby miss out on all kinds of fulfilling, satisfying, and fun experiences that God didn't let me have. Surely I would regret such a decision!" Have those kinds of thoughts crossed your mind occasionally? Are God's plans for us always in our very best interest? Couldn't we devise a more self-fulfilling life on our own?

To be convinced of God's good will toward me is the only way I can be moved to live a life of holy risk—of faith in God. A practical joker once reached out his hand to me in apparent friendship. I shook his hand—and got buzzed! But God is not going to fool us. In fact, according to the Scriptures, it's impossible to even imagine a better life than the one God will lead me into as I follow Him. "No mind has conceived what God has prepared for those who love him" (I Cor. 2:9). Thus, I want to come to the point in my prayers where I see that "what God gives" is the same as "what is the very best for me."

Application to Prayer

Learning more about the God to whom we pray will have a very wholesome effect on our praying, especially our desire to offer worship to Him. Our Lord's model prayer included the phrase "hallowed be your name." J. O. Sanders (*Prayer Power Unlimited*) writes of Dr. R. A. Torrey, who: "testified that an utter transformation came into his experience when he learned not only to pray and return thanks, but to worship—asking nothing from God, seeking nothing from Him, occupied with Himself, and satisfied with Himself. "

Organizing Your Personal Prayer Ministry

Look back now over the material you have explored in this lesson. Think first about the names of God. Then reflect on the attributes, or character of God. Add key ideas from your reflections to your prayer notebook. They will be valuable tools for your ongoing worship of God in prayer.

Last week you were asked to list all pertinent prayer requests and be praying for them daily. During this week continue developing this list. Ask the Lord to direct you in writing down the requests He wants you to hold in prayer. Pray also for the discipline needed for an effective prayer ministry. Be prepared to share your experiences, as well as any difficulties you may have encountered, with your group.

Organizing Your Prayer Ministry Team

Between now and your next group meeting, especially pray for the person who will become your Prayer Ministers Coordinator. *The success of this ministry will in large measure depend upon his or her performance.*

This person will:

1. Gather church-related requests for prayer, in cooperation with your church office. This information will be typed and made available to each Prayer Minister.

2. Contact the denominational or church group headquarters and receive their information for prayer regularly.

3. Arrange to receive prayer information from your church missionaries and other outreach ministries.

4. Contact one or more regional or national organizations to receive information for prayer.

5. Read this information as received from these sources and *highlight* key requests for prayer. Add this information to the other requests for prayer typed by your church staff.

The person who has agreed to serve as the Prayer Ministers Coordinator is:

_____

During your group meeting this week you should:

1. Finalize your plan for getting prayer request information to each of the group members weekly. This will require some organization and planning.

2. Select your Prayer Ministers Coordinator. Be sure that your pastor is in agreement with your selection.

Next week you should begin receiving requests weekly from your Prayer Ministers Coordinator.

(Note: Material on the names of God was adapted from Wayland Stephens Ministries, Olton, TX.)

4

WORSHIPING GOD THROUGH PRAYER

Holy, holy, holy . . .
Lord God Almighty,
who was, and is, and is to come. . . .
You are worthy, our Lord and God,
to receive glory and honor and power,
for you created all things,
and by your will they were created
and have their being.
(Rev. 4:8, 11)

A prayer direct from the heavenly choir! It's a prayer of praise—and a good model for us to practice here on earth, since we will be spending the vast portion of our existence throughout eternity doing the same thing: worshiping God (read Rev. 5:13 right now, and think it over). It's time to step back and remember: _The purpose of prayer should not be limited to making requests of God._

If we view our prayers as part of our total relationship with God, then surely there will be a balance between asking and praising. Jesus—by whose example we approach God as _Abba_ ("Daddy," Mk. 14:36)—also addressed His Heavenly Father in the modes of reverent worship. From the passages below, write out the words of praise that Jesus used in referring to God:

Matthew 6:9 _Hallowed is Thy name._

Luke 10:21 _Lord of heaven + earth_
John 17:11 _Holy Father_
John 17:25 _righteous Father_

With Jesus as our example, we are called to a life attitude of reverence before our Almighty God. But before we get specific about how to worship in prayer, let's look at two reasons why learning to worship is so important in the Christian life.

① Worship Pleases God

Christians want to please God! And it will become obvious that worship is pleasing to God when we recall what true worship really is. Here's a good definition to keep in mind: Worship means attributing worth to God. To put it simply, worship is saying things to God about His wonderful qualities and character. This is best accomplished when we talk TO God rather than ABOUT God. For example, little Johnny tells his friend: "My Daddy has big strong muscles!" This is simply a statement of information which could lead to more discussion. But when Johnny goes to Daddy face to face and says: "Wow, Daddy, you sure are strong!"—that's worship. (And Daddy enjoys it.)

Think about this definition in relation to your church worship services. By definition, sermons, announcements, or any part of a service *addressed to the congregation* should not be classified as worship in the strictest sense. The church is truly at worship when the assembly speaks directly to God in praise or thanksgiving regarding His matchless qualities.

Just for a short while, pretend you are in the place of God. From this perspective, evaluate the congregational worship that takes place during the Sunday morning service at your church:

I take issue with pressing this distinction regarding "strict understanding of worship." If anything done under the filling + unction of the H.S. + to the glory of God is worship. Preaching, Rom 12:1

Things we do that speak directly *to* God:

Singing praise + worship songs. Praying. Testimonies

Things we do that speak *about* God:

Sermon, Scripture reading. Singing testimony songs.

As a means of letting this strict definition of worship really sink in, give some careful thought to the words of hymns and prayers we use. Which are strictly worship (speak directly *to* God)? Which only talk *about* God? For example, the hymn: "Praise Him! Praise Him!" How would you change the wording to make it into worship?

Praise You! Praise You!

What about the children's prayer: "God is great; God is good"?

You are great; You are Good.

Amazingly enough, <u>our worship is a ministry to God Himself!</u> God is actively looking for those who know how to worship Him well. How do we know this? In John 4:23, Jesus says: "A time is coming and has now come when the true worshipers will worship the Father in spirit and truth, for they are the kind of worshipers *the Father seeks*."

What do you feel it means to worship God "in spirit"?

A deep commitment of the heart in the worshipper. Sincerity Honesty

What does it mean to worship Him "in truth"?

Although I wholeheartedly agree that we are sorely neglecting that activity that so pleases our Father of praising Him directly.

*Praying in agreement with truth
as it is about you, God, circumstances*

In the following exercise write down 10 qualities for which you think God would like to receive praise:

His sovereignty   *His patience*

His great grace   *His mighty power*

His wise plans   *His love of sinners*

His salvation   _____

His faithfulness   _____

Now stop reading for about five minutes and offer up a prayer of worship to the Lord. Use some of the qualities of God that you listed to minister to (or serve) God. "If anyone serves, he should do it with the strength God provides, so that in all things God may be praised through Jesus Christ. To . . . [You, God!] be the glory and the power forever and ever. Amen" (I Pet. 4:11).

Worship Satisfies the Soul

"What do you do during the day?" a friend asked an elderly Scotch woman who lived alone. "Well," she said, "I get my hymnbook and sing. Then I read the Psalms, meditating on God's greatness. When I get tired of reading and cannot sing anymore, I just sit still and let the Lord love me!"

The story simply illustrates that there is an aspect of worship that nurtures and ministers to *us*. When the Bible enjoins us to "be still, and know that I am God," we are privileged, through such meditative worshipfulness, to bask in the sense of God's awesomeness and love. Such sensations, though not to be expected—or necessarily sought—are a blessing of God's pure grace. And they can be part of the motivation for a life dedicated to praising prayer. Specifically, what happens, with regard to ourselves, when we worship?

WE GET OUR PERSPECTIVE BACK. Sometimes, in the midst of my busy life, I need a "reality check." It can be a real pressure to constantly function under the impression that everything depends on *me* —*my* abilities, *my* decisions. Bowing in a prayer of worship brings me back to the God who truly is THE ALMIGHTY. I remember His sovereignty over all things and situations. Being reminded of the finitude of this life and all its pursuits, I am encouraged by returning to the reality of my eternal Kingdom calling—and all the promises that go with it. Thus, through worship I find myself reequipped for spiritual battle.

WE ARE LED TO REPENTANCE AND RENEWAL. To focus for very long upon God's perfection, His all-consuming holiness, His infinite goodness, is to be led to repentance. Worship brings heartfelt revival! W. Bingham Hunter said:

I know of no significant spiritual revival which was not preceded by: (1) an increased awareness of the blinding whiteness of God's holiness; (2) a consequent desire by God's children to repent of and confess their sin; and (3) a firm resolution, with God's help and the encouragement of others, to pursue righteousness, faith, love and peace.
—*The God Who Hears* (Inter-Varsity Press)

WE FULFILL OUR CREATED PURPOSE. Though God does seek worship, and it pleases Him, we can see that worship is not purely for God's benefit alone. Actually, it is the very purpose for which we were created and granted salvation (for example, see the passages in the next paragraph). Thus, we would expect to find that when we worship, we are involved in one of the most fulfilling of all creaturely endeavors: to acknowledge our Creator and His overwhelming greatness.

The following New Testament passages speak about

the ultimate purpose for our existence: I Pet. 2:9; Eph. 1:11, 12; Phil. 2:10, 11. Meditate on these passages, then tell what practical sense of comfort you get from them as a believer:

Created to proclaim His excellencies; Created to be a source of praise of His glory; Every tongue designed to proclaim His sovereign glory. In worship I fulfill my ultimate purpose in being.

How to Worship in Prayer

In his very popular book *Ordering Your Private World* (Oliver-Nelson), Gordon MacDonald sums up the essence of worshipful prayer:

In our spiritual disciplines when we visit with the Father in the inner garden, adoration ought to be the first item on the worship agenda.

How can we worship in prayer? By first reflecting upon who God is and thanking Him for the things He has revealed about Himself. To worship in prayer is to allow our spirits to feast upon what God has revealed concerning His acts in the distant and recent past, and what He has told us about Himself. Slowly, as we review these things in a spirit of thanksgiving and recognition, we can sense our spirits beginning to expand, to take in the broader reality of God's presence and being. Slowly our consciousness is able to accept the fact that the universe about us is not closed or limited, but is in fact as expansive as the Creator meant for it to be. As we enter into worship we remind ourselves of how great He is

Get a sense of His grandeur

Like praying in general, the best way to learn how to worship God in prayer is to actually begin doing it. So, I am giving you five examples of fifteen minute personal worship sessions below, with suggestions on how to vary your approach. Perhaps you could try one each day for a week, or do one each week for five weeks. They are given only as suggested formats because <u>worship prayer is a personal encounter between you and your Creator.</u> You must find the way to approach God that you believe most pleases Him and seems satisfying to you as well. Also, remember that worship is the response of your whole self to God. You will notice that some of my suggestions try to help you remember to put your whole self into it—not just your mind.

(Note: Though the sessions focus on worship, I have no doubt that you will quite naturally feel led into confession and thanksgiving. Great! Follow the Spirit's leading.)

SESSION #1: PRAYING THE PSALMS.

Most of the psalms are actually prayers. Read Psalm 92 slowly as your personal prayer to God. Envision God's intimate presence with you and recite the words of praise to Him as your own sincere feelings. Suggestions:

1. Read the words slowly, aloud. Ruminate on the meaning and implications of what you are saying.

2. Try singing the psalm. Most psalms were originally set to music. Make up your own tune, even if it's a simple, repeating melody.

3. Your posture can help engender an attitude of praise. Try lifting your hands to Heaven. Kneel or bow down before the Lord. (Or, "fall down" before Him [see Rev. 4:10] by laying on the floor!)

4. Develop a list of your favorite praise psalms. For example: Psalms 24, 67, 90—98, 100, 113, 145, 148, 150.

SESSION #2: MEDITATING ON WHO GOD IS.

Choose one or more of God's attributes on which to meditate.

Suggestions:

1. Consider buying A.W. Tozer's classic, *Knowledge of the*

Holy. Read a chapter on one of God's attributes, then pray a prayer of worship revolving around how that attribute has been a blessing in your life. Give thanks for as many specific ways God has worked in your life, through that particular attribute, as you can.

2. Make use of silence. Do not be concerned about the words you are saying in your mind. Perhaps this time of praise will be more "wordless" than others. Sense God's love for you. (Praise to You!) Envision God's great power. (Glory to Your name!) Immerse yourself in the knowledge of His total sovereignty. (All honor to You!) Rest in His infinite grace. (Thou art worthy!)

3. Focus on Jesus—especially the glorified Christ. Read Revelation 4 and 5. Spend time praising the victorious Christ, whose Lordship every tongue shall someday confess. Begin now!

SESSION #3: USING THE HYMNAL.

Your favorite hymnal can be an excellent worship prayer aid. As you did with Psalm 92, use the hymn, "Holy, Holy, Holy! Lord God Almighty" as a personal song of praise to God. Suggestions:

1. By making small changes in wording, some hymns can be made to conform more to our strict definition of worship (speaking directly to God). Learn to change them by inserting a "You" in place of "Him" where needed. Also personalize the hymn, if necessary, by changing "we" and "us" to "I" and "me."

2. Develop your own list of favorite praise hymns. Some suggestions: "God Our Father, We Adore Thee," "Come, Thou Almighty King," "Lord of All Being, Throned Afar," "How Great Thou Art."

3. Make up your own hymns of praise. They don't have to rhyme in order to glorify God.

4. Memorize praise choruses used in your church services to use in your own private quiet time.

SESSION #4: USING WRITTEN PRAYERS OF PRAISE.

The following ascription of praise, known as the *Te Deum*, is an example of a traditional written prayer that has been used by Christians throughout the world. Perhaps it can sum up for you some of the things you would like to say to God. Use it as the basis of your worship time today.

You are God: I praise You;
    You are the Lord: I acclaim You.
You are the eternal Father:
    All creation worships You.

To You all angels, all the powers of Heaven,
    Cherubim and Seraphim, sing in endless praise:
Holy, holy, holy, Lord, God of power and might,
    Heaven and earth are full of Your glory.

The glorious company of apostles praise You.
    The noble fellowship of prophets praise You.
The white-robed army of martyrs praise You.

Throughout the world the holy Church acclaims You:
    Father, of majesty unbounded,
Your true and only Son, worthy of all worship,
    and the Holy Spirit, advocate and guide.

You, Christ, are the King of glory,
    eternal Son of the Father.
When You became man to set us free,
    You did not shun the Virgin's womb.

You overcame the sting of death
    and opened the kingdom of Heaven to all believers.
You are seated at God's right hand in glory.
    I believe that You will come, and be my judge.

Come, then, Lord, help Your people,
     bought with the price of Your own blood,
and bring us with Your saints
     to glory everlasting.

Suggestions:

1. Buy a book of prayers by an author who seems to be able to put into words your own deepest sentiments as you approach God. Using such prayers (occasionally) is like saying a sincere "Amen" to a fellow believer's prayer at a church service. That brother or sister is ministering to you as you minister to the Lord in worship.

2. Borrow a copy of *The Book of Common Prayer*. Try using its Morning and Evening Prayer services as your quiet time for a week. The Scripture readings and prayers in such services have stood the test of time for the edification of countless believers.

3. In your journal, practice writing out your own prayers of praise. Remember to focus on God's wonderful character and attributes.

SESSION #5: MOVING TO WORSHIP THROUGH CREATION.
     Worship outdoors while meditating on Psalm 8 or 19.
Suggestions:

1. Use a walk in the woods to prepare your heart and mind for worship. Read the psalm, and as you let your eyes fall on aspects of nature, offer up spontaneous praise to the genius of the Creator.

2. Spend some time out under the stars. Choose a clear night, preferably far from city lights. Can you see why David wrote: "When I consider your heavens, the work of your fingers, the moon and the stars, which you have set in place, what is man that you are mindful of him? . . . O Lord, our Lord, how majestic is your name in all the earth!" (Ps. 8:3, 4, 9.)

Your Ministry of Prayer

This week your Prayer Ministers Coordinator will provide you with your first weekly list of prayer requests from your church. This list will include such areas as:

•Regular or ongoing requests for the ministries of your church.

•Special needs and other requests on behalf of the church family.

•Note: If requests of a private or delicate nature are given to you, be sure and *treat these with the utmost of confidence*. Share them with no one, not even with members of your own family.

If for some reason this prayer request information from your church does not reach you this week, begin compiling your own list of church-related requests, using a copy of the form provided on page 119. Continue your ministry in prayer for needs on your daily list for prayer as well.

5

Let's pray for God's touch & help in this session

HINDRANCES TO EFFECTIVE PRAYER

Sing together

The earliest African converts to Christianity were known for the diligence with which they pursued their private devotions. Each one had a particular place in the brush where he would spend time meditating, praising, and making his requests known to God. The numerous paths to these private prayer sanctuaries became distinctly marked so that if anyone began missing his time of private devotions, others could soon tell. They would then remind him with words such as these: "Brother, the grass grows on your path."

Keeping the Path Clear *Reasons we fail to make time to pray.*

We could all point to various reasons for failing to have a more consistent prayer life, the most common being: "I just don't seem to have the time." And though we may make occasional efforts to find the time, the stark reality is that we must make the time to pray.

But why is it so hard to keep the grass from growing on our prayer paths? First, there is a primary theological reason—the flesh, the old nature, the dark presence of sin within us simply does not want to be exposed to the presence of God and His light. Even though we are indwelt by God's Spirit, there is still a part of us that rebels against the call to a disciplined, holy life. But take heart!

→ "flesh" = the personality of man under the control of sin and directed to selfish pursuits rather than the service of God.

The apostle Paul felt the same tug of the enemy, yet he knew there was a way out, too. Read about it now in Romans 7:14-25.

In what ways would you say your own struggles with the power of sin are similar to Paul's experience?

I allow my flesh to rule when I make excuses to neglect my inner life w/ God. I sometimes just don't think about it rather than making excuses.

How does this struggle relate to your present prayer life?

_____

_____

flesh is strong. Battle is hard. Just a knowledge of the law does not get me the victory.

Write your own paraphrase of the supremely positive part of this passage, in verse 25.

There is freedom from this life & death battle for control of my life in Jesus Christ my Lord and Him alone!

②A second broad reason our prayer paths tend to get overgrown has a psychological element—sometimes we would rather not admit that we, as mere human beings, are weak and dependent. We really do need our Heavenly Father, but are we willing to live like it? As Gordon McDonald (*Ordering Your Private World*) put it:

"I depend on God." Yet if I don't pray I am not depending on God.

We can say that we are weak people, and we can say that we depend upon God for all of our sustenance; but the fact is that something deep within us is not willing to recognize it. There is something deep within that vigorously denies our dependence.

Put your money where your mouth is.

Prayer calls us back to our relationship to God. Father and child, Shepherd and sheep, Lover and beloved—these are positions of dependence—these words symbolize our true relationship of dependence on God. Perhaps a lack of self-esteem makes us think: "I'm not really worthy of that kind of relationship with the God of the Universe." But because Jesus Christ shed His blood on our behalf, we *are*

• Admit weakness "I can do it myself"
  Act it out by praying - (act of dependence)
• Admit worth "I'm not worthy, yet."

worthy to approach Him with confidence, even in the midst of our weakness! What insight about this do you get from Hebrews 4:14-16?

I am of great concern to Him in this battle against heart-evil.

Barriers to Answered Prayer

We've spoken of two broad hindrances to effective prayer and praying, but now let's look at Scripture which gives us specific reasons why answers to prayer are hindered.

SIN. What key concept about *sin* keeps God from answering our prayers? (Psalm 66:18)

It disqualifies me from getting answers.

Look at Isaiah 59. What are some iniquities listed that keep God from hearing our prayers?

Lying; Evil talk; Unjust lawsuits; Deceptive presentation of your case; Confusing others; destroy by stealth (v.5); think evil; deny the Lord; Rebelling

What remedy has God provided that takes care of this problem? (I Jn 1:8, 9)

Confessed sin is forgiven + requalifies us.

DOMESTIC STRIFE. Now turn to I Peter 3:7, where a *domestic* issue is involved. This tells me that: *→ better*

I am not above her nor more important than her in the issues of life. The moment I take that position I nix God's power.

(For married group members: While this is a very personal matter, it is one with which we all need to deal. Just between the three of you [you, your mate and the Lord], the areas where you want the Lord's help include:)

Quit abdicating my position + letting her carry the spiritual ball.

Trusting God in spite of the circumstances.

Persevering in bleak situations.

Remaining visibly confident in God.

This is dishonoring to her. No asking her to carry load

Bring these matters to the Lord in prayer now. Next, take the appropriate action. It can make a *world* of difference in your prayer ministry!

LACK OF FORGIVENESS. What major barrier to answered prayer is dealt with by Jesus in Matthew 6:14, 15?

Forgiving others for their wrongs to me.

That is an awesome thought. Now turn to Matthew 18:21-35. What is the picture you get from this passage?

Although forgiveness is unearned it will be withheld if we are not merciful.

In commenting on these verses, J. O. Sanders (*Prayer Power Unlimited*) says: "These sobering words should convince us of <u>the folly of expecting an answer to our prayer when we are cherishing unforgiving spirits.</u> Because I have been forgiven, I must forgive. <u>If I fail to do so, I will be unable to pray with assurance of an answer.</u>"

Some additional hindrances to answered prayer include the following.

LACK OF FAITH. What *condition* for God answering our prayers is given in James 1:6?

Trusting God - w/o it we will not get expected results.

WRONG MOTIVES. What is another reason (Jas. 4:3) we sometimes do not get answers to our prayers?

selfishness

What is still another reason for unanswered prayer? (Prov. 21:13)

Ignore the needy.

<u>Of course, we are not saying that Christians cannot pray until every one of these problems ceases to exist in their lives. If that were the case, who could pray?</u> The Bible itself is full of examples of needy sinners (like us) who sought God through prayer. Like the distraught—but hopeful—

father of Mark 9:24, we can call out to God: "Lord, I do believe; help me overcome my unbelief!" The idea is to keep growing, keep confessing and being forgiven (I Jn. 1:9), and keep striving to overcome the hindrances. (Read Heb. 10:35, 36).

Most often, the best way to start and continue that process of overcoming is to share it with other believers—either another individual or a group. That's why your commitment to the LAMP group is so important. We also encourage you to establish an accountability relationship with another person, with whom you can pray or share prayer information. Mutual encouragement goes a long way toward increasing the effectiveness of your ministry of prayer.

To prepare for your time of group sharing, take the following steps. First, look back at the various hindrances covered in this lesson and pick your own most "bothersome" hindrance to effective praying. Write that problem here, with a brief description of when, where, and how it sabotages your prayer life:

In my sinful nature I blame God for making my life too busy. I don't make the time to pray to show Him He is being unfair with me. Also I struggle to focus in prayer.

Second, make some specific plans, or strategies, for beginning to overcome that hindrance on a daily basis. (For example, if you struggle with weariness, could you find a better time of day, pray out loud, pray while walking? Or if your mind wanders, what about giving yourself time before prayer to jot down the things you want to think about later, or keep a note pad with you to jot down intruding thoughts as they come up?) Be creative. What changes could you make to start overcoming those hindrances? Write your plans:

- Make a prayer list.

Confession & praise Personal, Family, Church, General
- Pray Every day.

or just the way things are.

- Remember that pressure is for my good.

Sometimes pressure my own't - lack disciplined planning: execution. Time pressure, emotional pressure, work pressure, ministry pressure, family pressure. And prayer is the only way to successfully handle pressure.

(Third,) share your plans with the group in your next meeting and ask for their feedback, suggestions, encouragement. As they respond, write down some of their most helpful comments here:

There is a place for "blaming" God — Getting it out of your system. But then move on, "God is God".

_____

_____

_____

_____

It's Worth It

In spite of the many reasons we might find for not praying, remember that there are overwhelmingly better reasons for making prayer a prime life priority. Jot down your insights after reading each of the following passages. Be prepared to share some of these insights in the group meeting.

Psalm 103:1-5 *His benefits: Pardon — Healing — Gives my life real value — changes my inner man — satisfies me —*

Proverbs 3:5, 6 *If I walk this road w/Him He will get me there. makes me strong*

Luke 18:1-8 *God is looking for those who will continue confidently as they await His timely + abundant answer.*

53

Luke 22:40 *Prayer brings strength to withstand temptation*

Philippians 4:6, 7 *What to pray for — everything what to worry about — nothing, Confident prayer brings peace of mind.*

Hopefully, you were encouraged by some of those Scripture gems. And we do need encouragement, especially when looking at the things holding us back from being all we want to be in the Kingdom. For example, most of us, if completely candid, could confess to a particularly bothersome "besetting sin" that seems to keep pummeling us just when we thought we had it licked. At those times, we're tempted to think that God has had just about enough of our constant failure to live up to His standards. And the most devastating result is that we may start shying away from prayer. We feel we have to "clean up our act" first. *But please don't fall into that trap.*

Here's a story that has helped me get untrapped. Maybe it can help you, too. It puts a very practical spin on the words found in Jeremiah 31:34: "I will forgive their wickedness and will remember their sins no more." It seems a young man had just come through a terrible onslaught of temptation. The Devil's withering darts had been flung at him from all sides—and he had succumbed to that same temptation—as he had done seemingly hundreds of times before. His heart was almost broken with his lack of willpower, and the last thing he thought he could do was come before God in such an "unclean" state. Nevertheless, he did sincerely ask God's forgiveness and determined to trust God for the strength he needed to change. Later that day, he felt a desire to pray again, and, remembering his former bout with sin, he began: "God, about that sin I keep falling into . . . ," but before he could continue, he sensed the voice of God speaking back to him: "*What* sin?"

God chooses to forget. Someone once said that God

54

really does bury our sins in the deepest sea—and He puts up a buoy with a sign that reads: "No fishing." Let us forget those things that God, by His gracious love, washes away by Christ's blood (see Tit. 3:5). Don't let past failures, no matter how many, keep you from coming to your Heavenly Father in daily prayer. He's patiently waiting for those times of fellowship with His beloved child—always.

Your Prayer Ministry

During your next weekly meeting you should receive a new list of church-related prayer requests from your Prayer Ministers Coordinator. Answers to prayer should also be noted on this sheet.

This week you are also to focus on requests for your personal ministry. This ministry may involve your neighbors, friends, people at work, and so forth. Wherever you are, you are touching the lives of others. This is your personal ministry. Ask that God will lead you in writing down requests that will advance His Kingdom in the lives of these people. A special form for recording these requests is provided on page 120 of this workbook.

A commitment to a significant ministry of prayer is not always easy. Paul reminds us:

Our struggle is not against flesh and blood, but against the rulers, against the authorities, against the powers of this dark world and against the spiritual forces of evil in the heavenly realms.

Pray in the Spirit on all occasions with all kinds of prayers and requests. With this in mind, be alert and always keep on praying for all the saints. (Ephesians 6:12, 18)

May God help you, guide you, and bless you in your ministry of prayer this week.

6

TOUGH QUESTIONS ABOUT PRAYER

Rick McKinnis, in an article in *Leadership*, tells about a small boy with cerebral palsy, named Joey. Rick, and his entire church had been praying for Joey. At one point, Rick's son asks him a pivotal question: "Daddy, what if Joey doesn't get better?"

The problem of this particular tragedy—as well as of all injustice, pain, and suffering in our world—is addressed in this lesson. Not that we will be able to answer all of the agonizing "whys." But perhaps some of the suggestions that follow will get you started on developing your own ways of making sense out of a world that can challenge our belief in God's goodness.

The secret things belong to the LORD *our God, but the things revealed belong to us and to our children forever, that we may follow all the words of this law* (Deut. 29:29).

When all is said and done, we need to step away from these issues and say, "I'm going to let God be God."

What about Apparently Senseless Suffering?

In response to Joey's question Rick writes:

He had asked one of the hardest questions of all. I told him I could not give a simple answer. I told him that many things (most things) about prayer and about how God works we don't understand very well. I explained that _evil_—things like sin and sickness and death—_were very strong in the world_, and God was _working against these things._ That was why He sent Jesus to live and die for us and to teach us of God's love and power. But I went on to say that not everything would be completely right until _Jesus came back to earth._ Then God's side, His Kingdom, would _win the final battle in the war against evil and hurtful powers._ We didn't know when Jesus would return to make things right, but until that time, _we were to work and pray for the good_ and _the right._

—"Confessions of A Skeptic," _Leadership_, Spring 1985.

Rick's answer is a good one because it focuses right away on the big picture that we spoke of in the first lesson of this course—giving his young son a view of the vast "behind the scenes" Kingdom where God's work and will are carried out.

What is your own way of making sense out of the suffering that exists in a good God's creation?

> While God is all-powerful + all loving He has decided to give man a free will. It is through man's choices of sin + selfishness that all evil has come into the world.

[margin note: ...ws us / e need / God.]

Everyone knows that intellectual answers and theological formulations seem inadequate and can sound trite when we are faced with the enormity of an _incurable disease, a_ natural _disaster_, or a _starving village._ But if I were asked for a "theology of suffering" here are some points I might build upon:

• Pain and suffering became a possibility with God's decision to create a world that allowed for _some level of both freedom of human choice_ (potential evil decisions), and _predictability_ (for instance, the unbending law of gravity). Thus, ultimately the evil, pain, and suffering in the world is largely the result of human choices that oppose God's will. Actually, then, it might be more reasonable to ask: "Why is there so much good in the world?" The answer is that God is gracious and long-suffering toward us.

•Let's also remember that, in many cases, good eventually results from suffering. It can be the "megaphone" of God to a fallen world—inducing both pity for those who suffer, and spiritual searching among those who would not otherwise be open to God's call.

•The worst pain and suffering have sometimes served as the setting to highlight the gemstone of God's overwhelming power of good over evil, love over hatred, and renewed faith over despair. For example, many people have suffered some of the most degrading conditions of hunger, cold, filth, and privation imaginable in Russian prisons. Surely it would seem difficult to find any evidence of God's goodness and power within such circumstances. Yet, consider the report of Anita Deyneka regarding God's surpassing brightness in the midst of such dark conditions:

Often Russian Christian [prisoners] quote a proverb, "The darker the night, the brighter the light," to describe the paradox of their position in Soviet society.

Miraculously, it is from this society, shrouded by atheism, that the Gospel is shining with a surprising radiance in the 1980's.

Malcolm Muggeridge noted this contrast when he said, "God always gives a sign relating to the particular situation in which we live. And for me the sign I see most clearly is that it is in the Soviet labor camps, in the most miserable conditions imaginable, that people have seen this light most brightly."

In the darkest of prison camps, God's light sometimes shines with dazzling power.

—Anita Deyneka, "God in the Gulag," *Christianity Today,* August 9, 1985

• Ultimately, the answer to suffering is the answer given to Job: "Will the one who contends with the Almighty correct him? Let him who accuses God answer him!" (Job 40:2). Our faith is that someday we will understand. Until then our task is to remind ourselves during the worst times that this world was never meant to be the best of existences. We live in a fallen world and long for a better one because there is one—Heaven, where every tear will be wiped from our eyes, and "there will be no more death or mourning or crying or pain" (Rev. 21:4b).

Why Pray, If God Knows What Will Happen?

This question reminds us of something very important: Our God is not bound by time. Our tendency is to think that God is waiting for tomorrow to happen, just like us. Not at all! God is the great I AM. He is in tomorrow, today, and yesterday all at once.

In light of God's existence outside of our limited, linear time framework, C. S. Lewis made the observation that if our prayers are granted, they are granted from the foundation of time. Our prayers are heard not only before we make them, but before we ourselves were made! When God created, He apparently took into account all the situations produced by the acts of His creatures, including our prayers, and somehow His will and ours are meshed together from eternity (for us, the beginning of time) in a matchless work of art known as God's plan for the ages. That plan involves goodness, allows for human freedom and evil, but ultimately results in the vindication of God's wisdom forever—"so that God may be all in all" (I Cor. 15:28c).

The Scriptural command to us to pray without ceasing means to persevere even though we cannot fully understand the mystery of how prayer works. No Christian would be justified in taking a position that says: "Until I can fully understand it, how can I do it?" Perhaps part of the joy of Heaven will be the insight we will get about the things that are so inscrutable to us now.

Can I Really Get God to Do Something?

Let's note that this question actually focuses on the nature of the relationship between *our* will and *God's* will. It is the classic question of human freedom and divine sovereignty. In trying to explain how these two work together, Christians have traditionally chosen to emphasize either one side or the other. But the plain fact is that human will and choices are apparently included in the outworking of God's sovereign plans—in ways that we can't fully explain.

Read the following verses and state the ways that you see human will (or actions) and God's sovereignty coming together:

II Kings 20:1-6 *Hezekiah's life was lengthened. God did it in response to Hezekiah's prayer.*

Matthew 26:16 compared with John 17:12 *Judas freely chose to accomplish what God had foreordained.*

John 6:35 compared with verse 65 *We are responsible to choose to come to Christ a yet that choice is somehow under God's control.*

Acts 2:23 *You chose to do this evil + are therefore culpable + yet God predetermined it to be.*

God both moves people into actions that fulfill His purposes, but at the same time He holds them responsible for the choices they make. And we can go on to say that human petition (our prayers) and divine sovereignty must fit together as well. In other words, God's plans and the working out of His will *include* our prayers and responses to Him.

Some have described the inter-relationship this way:

Divine Sovereignty + human prayers fit together Divine Sovereignty + human choices fit together

I· God grants us the privilege of being a means. Prayer has been ordained by God as a means to accomplish aspects of His will. Thus, in a sense, the question, "Can I really get God to do something?" is not a proper one since it assumes that we are in a completely separate subject-object relationship with God—that one is the "worker" (the person who tries to influence God) and the other is the "worked upon" (God, who is influenced). But God is not a mere object for us to try to influence or change. We are intimately related as creature to Creator.

Read Romans 8:26, 27. What part does the Holy Spirit play in your prayers?

He converts our longings + desires into those that are agreeable to the plan + will of God.

In what ways does His praying suggest a pattern prayer? How can that pattern become effective?

The Spirit can pray according to the will of God bc He is close to God

II· Another way to approach the question "Can I really get God to do something?" is to look closely at Jesus' extreme statements about prayer in the gospels. Read some of them now, and paraphrase them in your own words below:

Matthew 21:22 *If you don't doubt, you will receive what you ask for.*

Mark 11:24 *Confidence in God that what you ask for will happen is required.*

John 14:14 *Anything asked in line with Christ + His will will be given.*

John 16:23 *God grants our prayers because of Christ's purposes*

Answer—pag 65

How do you understand these statements? Are they exaggerated to make a point? Do they represent the great unused key to unlock any difficult or even impossible situation? If so, why have Christians not used them more effectively to change our world for God?

What is your own understanding of these promises?

_____

_____

Remember, each of Jesus' extreme statements about prayer was directed to a specific group of people: the disciples. Could it be that the closer we come to Christ in our own daily personal discipleship, and the more we know of *His* character, *His* plans, *His* will, the closer we will come to praying *according* to that will? And therefore the more likely our requests will be granted? Chances are the disciples had a good idea about which prayers would further the Kingdom, and which were merely selfish or presumptuous.

The point is simply this: Our prayers are not to be something tacked onto our lives as another duty or habit that we carry out. Actually, getting answers to prayer probably has more to do with *who we are* than what we say.

Yet Jesus' words still stand. The disciple who prays—I repeat: the disciple—gets what he or she prays for. The pattern, then, is this: as we are becoming better disciples, more of our praying is in line with God's will, and more of our prayers are being answered. Again, the question, "Can I really get God to do something?" is not a proper one—since our true goal is not to change God, but more and more, to let God change us, and then work through us.

What About Unanswered Prayer?

A minister friend of mine once developed a sermon outline on prayer that went like this: "Go! No! Slow!" His

62

point was that God always answers our prayers—either with a yes, a no, or a call for us to wait on His wise timing. It is easy to see the truth in this, especially if we remember that many of our prayers can only be fully answered in eternity, when God's Kingdom comes to full fruition forever (see I Cor. 15:24-28). For example, our prayers for peace, justice, cessation of suffering, and worldwide adoration of Christ will apparently have to wait for their fullest answer.

But I am assuming that the question is asked specifically about those prayers that we have every reason to believe are both in accord with God's revealed will and very reasonably answerable in the present time. Why doesn't a good, wise God do something now about these kinds of requests? Why would God say "no" or "wait" to a request for funds to buy Bibles for a foreign missions project, or a request for a job for an unemployed Christian steel worker whose family is on welfare? Yet we all know of examples in which God's apparent silence is deafening.

Take time to read through the short Book of Habakkuk right now, then answer the following:

People who seem to be a thorn in God's side are not stopped.

belief,
isdom,
ection,
liverance
es not
one.

Share a time when you could identify with the prophet's pleading for God to intervene in verses 1:2-4.

That my parents would have a deep and life-changing respect for the Truth of God! I have prayed & yearned for it.

In what ways can you relate to the prophet's statement of renewed faith in verses 3:17-19?

They are a part f liberal methodism

1) One day ~~every~~ them knees shall bow to the Truth 2) Funeral service w/ power 3) My being in their family proves God has a plan to influence them.

All of us can relate to having had the feeling that our prayers appear to be going unanswered. But realize that we often only *think* our prayers have gone unanswered. Our supremely wise God may answer in His own unique, creative ways—of which we remain unaware.

And we really do prefer God's wisdom to our own, don't we? Think back over your lifetime of prayer so far. Can you think of any prayers that you are now sincerely thankful that God didn't answer the way you wanted? Share:

Prayed to someday marry the wrong girl.

Foundational to all praying is the belief that God really does have our best interest at heart. It's not a fight: to convince Him I'm worthy; to convince Him that things would be better if only I were happy; to convince him of the wisdom of my solutions. Rather, it is a call to a loving Father to relate to me. And He will relate. "I will take care of you," He says. Though sometimes it will be in silence, "I will be with you always," remains His promise. And we all know that there are times when not even answers could be better than a loving arm around the shoulders.

Here's a suggestion on how to use this chapter's material through interacting with another believer. Pick someone you respect as a wise, mature Christian—perhaps from your church—and ask for a brief interview. Ask this person how he or she would answer one or two of the questions dealt with in this chapter. Then just listen. Bring your notes from the interview to the group meeting, and share how your thinking about these questions has been influenced by the information in this chapter, or by the interview experience.

Your Ministry of Prayer

Our special prayer focus this week relates to your work. List on page 121 (or in your prayer notebook) those key work-related requests, such as your efficiency, testimony, satisfaction, or future on the job. Pray also for your fellow employees. Ask God for help in developing relationships with them that may lead to their conversion to Christ.

If you are retired, or unemployed, or work at home, list requests that relate to how you spend your time each day. Ask God concerning priorities, goals, effectiveness, ministry to others, and so forth.

During your group meeting this week you should again receive an updated list of prayer requests from your Prayer Ministers Coordinator.

Isaiah records an amazing statement of our Lord—to a nation wallowing in wickedness of every kind:

> *He saw that there was no one, he was appalled that there was no one to intervene* (Isaiah 59:16).

It can be different in our day. People who pray can make that difference.

I do not believe these promises are an exaggeration. I believe they show that 1) prayer is a mystery. Somehow a sovereign God has chosen to incorporate my prayers + not violate either His sovereignty or my freedom. Through prayer God has granted us the privilege of being the _means_ of accomplishing His will. 2) As we draw closer to God + pray w/o doubt are empowered to desire in agreement w/ His will + this unlocks the power of God.

Why is this not done more? Because this takes personal transformation (moving closer to God) and time + experience in praying.

7

JESUS PRAYS

Did Jesus really need to pray? After all, He was the Son of God, wasn't He? Why would He need to pray? Couldn't He merely *will* something to be done—and have it done? The answer to such questions is shrouded in the mystery of the incarnation. *During the incarnation He voluntarily took a subjective position.*

While Scripture teaches that Jesus was "in very nature God," nevertheless He also was "made in human likeness and . . . found in appearance as a man" (Phil. 2:6-8). "The whole testimony of the gospels," J. O. Sanders (*Prayer Power Unlimited*) says, "leads to the view that His deity in no way affected the reality of His human nature. The only difference is that He did not sin. His prayers were *as real and intense as those of any other man*." Thus the prayers of Jesus were in some respects not unlike the prayers that we can and ought to make as Christians. The study of Jesus' life in regard to prayer is instructive and inspiring. *Phil 2:6-8 Kenosis*

A Voluntary set aside of Divine peregatives

Where Did Jesus Pray?

Jesus would withdraw from the heavy demands of His public ministry in order to pray. Finding quiet places for prayer was not always easy. How was Jesus able to find a solitary place for prayer according to:

Mark 1:35? *He got up early & went off alone.* *People put off.*

People waited → *People seem to be put off.*

Matthew 14:13? *He got in a boat + physically removed himself*

Matthew 14:23? *He sent people away + went to a place of seclusion.*

What does Luke 5:16 teach us about the frequency of these times of private prayer?

It was often. LK 6:22 - The whole Night

Jesus was intensely busy. He was ministering to people—training the disciples, healing the sick, and preaching to the crowds almost constantly. <u>Yet He regularly</u> found the time and place for extended seasons of prayer. <u>What are the lessons for you here?</u>

Prayer took priority over the needs of people
Pray apart from the noise of life.

Before leaving this thought, let your mind do a double take on this verse: "<u>Once when Jesus was praying in private</u> and his disciples were with him"(Lk. 9:18). How do you figure that one out? Apparently Jesus' power of concentration was such that He was able to shut out distractions around Him in order to give Himself to prayer. Could we try that on some occasions? How about when driving to or from work? Or when doing mundane household chores? Or when the kids are playing? Or?

"Busy" times when I could fit in prayer include:

Building computers.

How Did He Pray?

We may wonder about the correct posture in prayer. What was Jesus' position while praying in:

Matthew 14:19 *Looking up to heaven.*

Luke 22:41 *He knelt down.*

Matthew 26:39 *Layed ~~d~~ on the ground face down.*

Not position but submission.

What does this seem to teach us about the "correct" position in which to pray?

There is no one correct position

Perhaps there's another lesson here too. If the very Son of God got down on His knees, and even on His face, what does this teach us about *how* He prayed?

In all of Jesus prayer there was heart intensity that could be seen in His physical positions in prayer.

Why Did Jesus Pray?

What circumstances called for prayer in each of the following passages, and with what results? *—just before a new day of battle*

Mark 1:32-37 *The completion of a day of spiritual battle.*

Luke 3:21, 22 *During His baptism; Heaven revealed His iden* — *Reverence*

Luke 6:12, 13 *When attacked; Before making serious decis*

Luke 9:28-36 *Jesus & 3 disciples alone together; Importance of* — *Glory revealed* — *prayer*

John 11:38-42 *this Prayer assumes an answer. Weak faith called forth strong, confident pub prayer*

If Jesus needed to pray—and pray most earnestly and continually—what message does this communicate to us, and of our need to be men and women of prayer?

In battle, in worship, when attacked, & making serious decisions; w/ others; in public

What Did Jesus Pray?

In John 17, we see Jesus at prayer. This was for Him an unparalleled time of stress. The time for His departure had grown near. Look carefully at this passage, especially to learn about *our* ministry of prayer.

JESUS PRAYS FOR HIMSELF. Read John 17:1-5. What was Jesus' prayer for Himself?

That in this greatest hour of trial Jesus would glorify God.

There is a connection b/t prayer
& the manifestation of God's
glory - Transfiguration, Baptism, Jn 17:

How and when was this prayer answered?

Through Christ's voluntary death and victorious
resurrection God was glorified. _Jesus restored_
to glory
Hatred of sin, love of mankind & Willingness to save.

Being glorified meant Jesus' return to His former exalted state as God in Heaven. His prayer saw through His coming death, to the triumph and glory which was to follow.

How is this theme brought out in Hebrews 12:2?

_____

_____

Look again at John 17:4. Think how you will apply this prayer personally. How will it affect your living? Your praying?

Live & pray to glorify God

_____

JESUS PRAYS FOR HIS DISCIPLES. In verses 6-19, Jesus intercedes for His disciples—for those He called His friends and brothers. Read this section now.

Why was Jesus _focusing_ prayer on His disciples?

He was going to leave them + knew
they needed God's help

What were two concerns in His prayer for them?

P _rotect_ _____ them;

S _anctify_ _____ them.

Praying that God would protect His followers—especially as His own crucifixion was now imminent—was the most strategic prayer that He could make. The very existence of the Church and its future growth was dependent on this prayer being answered. These disciples _had_ to be kept from the onslaught of persecution which was sure to come. They _had_ to survive—for God's Church was within them!

The Greek word for the "S" word above is *hagios*, which means "set apart to or by God, consecrated; holy, morally pure, upright." It is frequently used in Scripture of God's people.

And just as important, they had to be made holy, for God's work on earth is holy, and the holy God works through sanctified men and women.

How can Paul's prayer in I Thessalonians 5:23 serve to strengthen your praying for God's people in this area?

This is God's will for us.

Look at the thrust of Jesus' prayer for His disciples from our perspective today. What lesson, or lessons does it have for our praying? How will it guide the way we pray for others?

These are our two greatest needs.

JESUS PRAYS FOR FUTURE BELIEVERS. Jesus concludes His prayer, in John 17:20-26, with intercession for all who *will* come to believe in Him. Read through this section and answer the following questions.

What is the main thrust of Jesus' request on behalf of all believers? *in context of Truth*
unity / not uniformity

What is the intended result, or purpose of this request?
The world would take notice of Jesus Christ

Jesus prays that believers may be one so that the world will know that He came from the Father. While it is not necessarily *organic* unity that Jesus has in mind, certainly it is a *spiritual* unity, a unity of heart and purpose. He wants all of His people—those born of the Spirit, filled with His love and indwelt by Christ Himself (John 17:26),

70

to be at *one* even as the Father and the Son are one (vs. 21).

Make a list below of specific intercessions that you could pray as a way of contributing toward Christian unity.

_____

_____

_____

_____

_____

_____

_____

_____

Isn't it wonderful that you and I are on Jesus' prayer list? As a means of reminding yourself daily of this great encouraging truth, memorize the following passage: "Therefore he is able to save completely those who come to God through him, because he always lives to intercede for them" (Heb. 7:25).

Your Ministry of Prayer

In light of Jesus' "high priestly" prayer in John 17, are there other names or needs that should be added? Write down the things you will include—indeed, emphasize—as you intercede for others.

This week you are asked to prepare a separate prayer list for your own immediate family and relatives. Many of these requests may already be on your daily list for prayer. You may want to add other requests this week, some of which can be on this list you will pray for at least weekly.

Think through each family member and write out key requests for each. Update your list on a regular basis and, as with your other prayer lists, record answers to prayer both for your encouragement and to give praise to God. For your convenience, you may make a copy of the form on page 122 to record these requests for your family.

Your Prayer Ministers Coordinator will also provide you with the latest update of church-related requests.

8

JESUS TEACHES US TO PRAY

Those first disciples were impressed by the prayers of their Lord—how He prayed, and got answers! So they asked: Lord, how should we pray?

In the centuries that have gone by since, the Lord's Prayer (Matthew 6:9-12) has become the most used prayer of all time. And its lessons are of timeless worth. Learning from Jesus is vital to the effectiveness of our ministry of prayer. Before studying the prayer itself, notice the words of caution from Matthew 6:5-8.

How does the negative example in verse 5 relate to praying today?

When the purpose of my prayer is self-image. I use my prayer as a means to elevate myself.

Why does Jesus tell us to pray in a private place? (vs. 6)

To avoid selfish temptations. To enable (b/c our hearts are sinful) us to pray selflessly.

How might Christians today fall into the error of the "pagans"? (vs. 7)

Mindless repitition of liturgy. Saying the same thing over & over again each

John R. Stott (*Christian Counter-Culture*, InterVarsity

time we pray. Using the same old phrasings & cliches w/o thinking about them.

73

Press) skillfully summarizes the significance of this prayer in the context of Jesus' general instructions:

> The so-called "Lord's Prayer" was given by Jesus as a model of what genuine Christian prayer is like . . . in distinction to the prayers of Pharisees and heathen. To be sure, one could recite the Lord's Prayer either hypocritically or mechanically or both.
>
> _The error of the hypocrite is selfishness._ Even in his prayers he is obsessed with his own self-image and how he looks in the eyes of the beholder. But in the Lord's Prayer Christians are obsessed with God—with his name, his kingdom and his will, not with theirs. True Christian prayer is always a preoccupation with God and his glory. . . .
>
> _The error of the heathen is mindlessness._ He just goes babbling on, giving voice to his meaningless liturgy. He does not think about what he is saying, for his concern is with volume, not content. But God is not impressed by verbiage. Over against this folly Jesus invites us to make all our needs known to our heavenly Father with humble thoughtfulness, and so express our daily dependence on him. Thus Christian prayer is seen in contrast to its non-Christian alternatives.

Glance again at Matthew 6:5-8. How might your praying be affected by selfishness?

In order to avoid mindless babble I sometimes don't pray. (Prayer list praying)
_e.g._
Correction - Mindless praying is not paying attention to what I'm

How might it be affected by mindlessness? _praying, not praying about it earlier th._

Praying long prayers.

Jesus' Model Prayer

I am <u>struck with how few words Jesus used</u> in His teaching on prayer, including this <u>model prayer</u> that He gave us. Most of us, if given the chance, would have much more to say. But Jesus cut through the human tendency to indulge in abstruse explanation and speculation. He gets right to the point: The Son tells us how to communicate with the Father! We will no doubt want to listen—and learn.

OUR FATHER IN HEAVEN. The prayer begins with a recognition of God as Father. He is the Father of all those who are born into His family by trusting Christ as Savior.

How is this important truth brought out in John 3:3-5?

It teaches that it requires a birth apart from the physical birth, that comes from God to put one in God's family.

Concerning this first phrase, Sanders, in *Prayer Power Unlimited*, summarizes:

"Our Father" awakens love in our hearts; "Who art in heaven" engenders awe. And these together constitute worship. The invocation is a blending of intimacy and majesty.

HALLOWED BE YOUR NAME. God's name is God's character. His concern for His name is evident in the following Old Testament passages.

How is God's name honored? (Lev. 22:2)

By worshipping Him with clean hands.

What does God promise those who do not revere His name? (Deut. 28:58, 59)

He will turn against them.

How is the holiness of His name to be known to the world? (Ezek. 36:23)

His holiness is to be displayed through His people.

How can this teaching affect your prayer ministry?

75

I should pray in an attitude of reverential respect.

YOUR KINGDOM COME. Scripture indicates both a present and a future manifestation of God's kingdom.?

The saving, transforming reign of God.

What *focus* do the following passages give to your ministry of prayer?

join His Kingdom

John 3:3-5 *Men cannot relate to Him as Father until there is a radical transformation, a generation of new life (the new-birth) in them. This is the to in.*

✓ *Tells us how*

Romans 14:17 *God's kingdom is a kingdom where Jesus ? here His Kingdom (righteousness, peace, & joy) are present Comes*

I Corinthians 4:20 *God's transforming (power) to be unleashed*

Matthew 9:35-38 *God to thrust out laborers, herders to save the sheep & bring in the harve*

Luke 17:20-21 *Pray for generation of new transforming life w/in people.*

Record this prayer focus information in the appropriate place in your prayer notebook. <u>Praying on the basis of Scripture can</u> mean praying with conviction and power. There is a future aspect of the Kingdom as well, when the reign of Christ will be over all the earth. <u>Our praying should also include both thanksgiving and prayer for that Kingdom.</u>

YOUR WILL BE DONE. Here is a tremendously important key to the Christian life. This <u>life can be a battleground of wills.</u> Is it <u>our will</u>, or <u>His will</u>? How we respond in this area can make a significant difference in the Kingdom of our Lord.

Express your desires in this regard as you look at Psalm 40:8.

Whatever it takes, Lord.
I am willing.

I want God's will to be the
delight of my life & spring from my
deepest sentiments

How will this aspect of the Lord's prayer guide your prayer times for others?

I will pray for God's will in their
life knowing that is best for them.

Moving on in the prayer, we note that the essential needs of personhood are covered in the following three phrases: "Give us today our daily bread" anticipates our physical needs; "forgive us our sins" speaks to our psychological needs; and "lead us not into temptation" anticipates our spiritual needs.

GIVE US TODAY OUR DAILY BREAD. Here is our admission that <u>we depend on God to supply each of our needs</u>. Looking at our immediate needs—this very day—<u>no request is too small to be brought before our Provider.</u>

List some of your current and long-term needs.

Physical: *Increase strength, energy, + stamina.*

Material: *Pay off debts; provide for future needs (college; retirement;* *$180/wk cut in wages*

meet current needs + of course longer use Vocational: *Follow God regardless of vocational consequences.*

Psychological: *Peace & total trust* *Heb 3, 4*

Social: *More effective in friendship evangelism; Develop friendships w/Christ*

Others: *Grow academically*

In what ways is God already supplying your needs in these areas?

— Gift from Kathy's Mo[...]

Given time off work for exercise. Computer knowle[dge] thru job @ Agri-Logic; Kathy's book business; Friendship of John, Jim, Robert

In which areas do you believe God may be wanting you to either work or wait for those needs to be supplied?

Start Computer business; Wait on vocational questions; Pursue Barry, Teresa + others

In which areas do you see a need for continued petitioning for God to intervene on your behalf?

Business; vocational

Who else might God use to help supply your needs in some of the areas mentioned?

No matter how you answered the preceding four questions, the point is that <u>God's children have no need to look into the future with fear, or to be filled with worry</u>. As the old gospel hymn puts it:

> *Be not dismayed what e'er betide,*
> *Beneath His wings of love abide,*
> *God will take care of you.*

Read Matthew 6:25-34. Paraphrase the theme of this passage in your own words, substituting three of your own words (that show your current life concerns) in place of "eat," "drink," and "wear." (For example: "Therefore I tell you, do not worry about your life, how you will pay for graduate school, whether your children will be safe at play, or when your promotion will come through..." etc.)

Therefore I tell you, do not worry about your life, how you will pay off your debts, how your convictions will be responded to, how you will provide for your future (college house independence)
Remember the Ant.

Did this exercise help you sense God's peace and comfort in the midst of your problems? If so, how?

Yes, because God has promised He is involved & He will provide either solutions or grace + peace to weather the problems in His strength.

FORGIVE US . . . AS WE ALSO HAVE FORGIVEN . . . . Two matters of extreme importance are: obtaining forgiveness from God, and dealing with our tendency not to forgive others. Jesus tells us there is a link between our relationship to God, and our treatment of others. How shall we understand this relationship, based on Matthew 6:14, 15?

barrier us + God.

If we are unforgiving to others then God is not forgiving toward us.

Remember that God's forgiveness comes unconditionally to those who repent. This is possible because of the work of Jesus on the cross in our behalf. Our sins were fully atoned for in that gracious demonstration of His love for us. Thus, no act of ours can earn God's forgiveness.

Yet, we are called to forgive others. This is probably because God only forgives the truly penitent—and surely this must include our willingness to "let others off the hook" in light of God's super-abounding mercy toward us.

What is the main point of the parable in Matthew 18:21-35? How does it affect you? Your prayers?

To refuse to forgive brings personal torment & paralysis and affects Christ's reputation

As one young Sunday School scholar prayed: "Forgive

Cost of forgiveness
Cost of unforgiveness

God is sovereign

us our trashbaskets as we forgive those who trashbasket against us." Jesus is simply saying that if we are holding a grudge about somebody's "trashbasket" toward us, how can we sincerely come before our Father in complete repentance? We must forgive others—as hard as that may seem. Here is how Carroll Simcox (*Prayer: the Divine Dialog,* Inter-Varsity Press) helpfully defines the task:

> *Sometimes you have to forgive doggedly and only out of obedience; you cannot do it gleefully. But if you do it with your will, and pray that love for the offender will fully repossess your heart, you will be given growth in the very charity of God.*

It can be a real help, when struggling to forgive someone, to take a close look at your own actions toward someone else—especially when your action has been similar to the one that has injured you. Right now, see if you can fill in the columns below from either present or past experience:

Someone who sinned against me:

What he/she did:

_____

_____

_____

Have I forgiven this person?

_____

My next step:

_____

_____

_____

Someone I have sinned against:

What I did:

_____

_____

_____

Have I received forgiveness from this person and God?

_____

My next step:

_____

_____

_____

A well-wishing prayer that I hope to be able to pray for

that person (by God's grace) in the future:

_____

_____

_____

If this exercise has proven enlightening, don't stop there. Consider taking the action steps required to convey your decision to extend forgiveness to those who have wronged you. Then come to God and be forgiven! The goal is to be fully reconciled to God and others.

AND LEAD US NOT INTO TEMPTATION, BUT DELIVER US FROM THE EVIL ONE. The Greek word here for "temptation" is also translated elsewhere in the Bible with words like "trial," "testing," "trying circumstance." The *New English Bible* translates: "Do not bring us to the test" (Mt. 6:13). We know that God does not tempt us to do evil (Jas. 1:13), but He may allow our faith to be tested through the trials that come our way.

This part of the Lord's prayer gives explicit recognition to our inability to stand against the "principalities and powers" of evil without God's protection and deliverance.

According to I Corinthians 10:13, what are two of God's promises to us when we are tempted? (Note: Try to memorize this verse before your next group meeting.)

He will limit it.

He will enable you to handle it.

Romans 13:14 states (in the NASB): "Make no provision for the flesh." Some specific areas of temptation for me:

Stay up late (can't get to sleep)

Procrastinate

What it means for me to "make no provision" for these temptations (i.e., ways I can plan to avoid being in a position of being tempted):

Have time w/ Lord b/f bed. Set a bedtime
& stick to it. Make daily To Do list & do it
in order of priorities.

Read Ephesians 6:10-18. Which parts of the Christian armor do you find yourself wearing most of the time?

Truth - I have the courage to stand on
my convictions in both work. Righteousness
Truthfulness
I work at maintaining a clean
conscience + good relationships

With which parts do you feel you need to "dress yourself" more completely?

Preparation   Faith   Prayer

Notice that prayer concludes this passage, Ephesians 6:18. In your own words, how does this verse say you are to pray?

In dependence on Spirit to guide, & empower
your prayer bringing before the Lord all
relevant petitions that you discern as your

FOR YOURS IS THE KINGDOM AND THE POWER AND THE GLORY FOREVER. AMEN. Finally, we are brought back to the core of our Christian existence. For us, God is to be revered as all-in-all because that is truly His position in the universe. With this concluding burst of praise, we remind ourselves to order all our priorities to be consistent with God's eternal reign.

Your Ministry of Prayer

Each week now you will be receiving a complete list of updated prayer requests. Do encourage your Prayer Ministers Coordinator in this vital, *extra* ministry undertaken in behalf of Christ and His Kingdom. Thank your pastor, too, and other involved church staff members.

This week your Prayer Ministers Coordinator should provide you with requests which he or she has selected from your denomination or church group headquarters. These requests are added, in a separate category, to the list you are now receiving weekly through your church office.

daily monitor your world. You are to persevere in these matters trusting God + petitioning God.

9

LEARNING FROM THOSE WHO PRAYED

An old English proverb says: "Example is better than precept." In other words, sometimes the best way to learn a thing is to watch someone else do it. Of course, it's best if that person serves as a *good* example, but it is possible even to learn by observing those who do it all wrong.

Enlightening Exercise

Most of the Biblical pray-ers serve as positive models, and their praying is invaluable instruction for our own growth in the life of prayer. Take a look for yourself by doing the exercise below. You may want to read the context of these prayers in order to get a clearer picture.

Pray-er: Abraham, Genesis 18:16-33

Primary Request:

He asked God to spare Sodom & Gom. for the sake of the righteous living there

Why did Abraham not receive the answer to this prayer?

God had a different plan to save Lot.

What lesson is there in this for me?

You need to persevere in prayer even if the answer is no.

Don't put God in a box.

Pray-er: David, II Samuel 7:18-29

Primary Request:

David first expresses his amazement + gratitude for His merciful blessing upon His servant + people. He prayed that God would do as He had promised + establish His kingdom + thereby be magnified in the world.

How can I apply this in my prayer ministry?

David claimed + pleaded the clear promises of God as the basis of his prayer requests. So should I.

Pray-er: Ezra, Ezra 9:1-15

Primary Request:

Confession of the sins of the people.

Lessons about prayer which I can apply are:

Somehow there is an appropriateness with my association with the sins of my people even though if I'm innocent.

Pray-er: Jonah, Jonah 4:1-11 (especially vs. 3)

For what did Jonah pray?

That God would take his life.

What does this prayer teach me *not* to do?

Not to hold lightly what God highly values. †

Pray-er: Jesus, Matthew 26:36-46

What was the content of Jesus' prayer?

That God might provide some other way than the substitutionary death. To spare Christ from the cross.

† If it be morally consistent with God's redeeming purpose.

→ matt. 27:46
y alternative to sin-bearing fering on the route to fulfill the there's redemptive purpose.

85

→ That's what Jesus desires but more deeply still He desires to do the Father's will.

In what ways will this guide my praying?

_I can come to God
pursuing other options but
I must be willing to accept His
answer_

Pray-er: A beggar, Luke 18:38-42

What did he request?

Physical healing

What prayer principles can be applied?

• _Don't let obstacles stop your persistance
in prayer._ • _Others might not
agree that your prayer is legitimate_
• _Response: follow + glorify Christ_

There! Be prepared to share both the positive and negative principles you learned with your study group. Especially focus on principles you can apply in your own prayer life.

Enduring Examples

Now let's zero in on a few more of the well-known Scriptural examples of approaches to prayer. This time, I will share what I see as the basic principle involved. And since I have done this part of the work, it's your task to go a step further (from head and heart, to *hands*) by thinking of concrete ways that you could begin practicing that principle in your prayer life—and even sharing it with someone else. You may not be able to start implementing all of them at once. But be open to the Spirit's leading regarding one or more areas that may be especially relevant to your present level of praying and begin practicing them right away.

A SERVANT—Genesis 24:12-27. Theme: guidance. Principle: *Our prayers for guidance must be linked to a willingness to get involved.*

Notice that the servant was not one to stay in his closet and pray for guidance without immersing himself in the action. We know that there is a time to wait upon God. But the servant knew he was commissioned by God (through Abraham) to accomplish a particular task. Thus, he developed a plan of action and proceeded, asking God to guide him. To use a nautical analogy: When we pray for God to steer our boats along the right course, let us make sure that our sails are raised!

JACOB—Genesis 32:24-30. Theme: perseverance. Principle: *God values our prayerful persistence.*

But perhaps there is a sense in which God does wish to see just how seriously we take His Word and the things of His Kingdom. In the New Testament, the teaching of Jesus emphasized the value of not giving up. (Right now read and meditate on Luke 11:5-10; 18:1-7.) Our increasing ability to persevere in prayer also strengthens our spiritual growth in discipline, commitment, and patience.

HANNAH—I Samuel 1:9-11. Theme: earnestness in prayer. Principle: *God hears no more than the heart speaks.*

That's a pretty common saying, but isn't it true? Hannah, "in bitterness of soul . . . wept much and prayed to the Lord." And the Lord "remembered" her. (Also read Heb. 5:7, where you will see Jesus as one who poured out His heart to God, too.) Since God sees and hears our innermost feelings, there's certainly no use in trying to cover up those feelings before Him. It's unfortunate that often our lips are saying one thing, while our hearts communicate something quite different.

And even when we don't really know our own hearts, we can be greatly encouraged by the fact that the Holy Spirit does! Take a moment to paraphrase in your own words the incredible truths you find in Romans 8:26, 27:

God, the Holy Spirit, having a deep understanding of our hearts, prays for us in great earnestness and in line with God's perfect will.

JEHOSHAPHAT—II Chronicles 20:6-12. Theme: help in crisis. Principle: *In crisis, prayer ought to be the first—not the last—resort*.

Jehoshaphat was told that an enemy army was getting ready to attack. How did he respond? "Alarmed, Jehoshaphat resolved to inquire of the Lord . . . ." How different from the old maxim: "When all else fails, you can always pray."

DANIEL: Daniel 9:1-19. Theme: prayer and fasting. Principle: *Fasting heightens the intensity of our praying*.

Daniel was extremely burdened for the plight of Jerusalem during the Babylonian captivity. And he wanted to be sure that God too felt the impact of his concerns and special requests. Have you ever felt like that?

Christian broadcaster David Mains says you are in the target group for fasting if "you have an intense desire for God to show Himself sufficient in terms of meeting a pressing need, if you seek assurance regarding the Lord's thoughts about a major decision, if you're especially anxious for the welfare of a loved one, if you feel under constant, heavy enemy bombardment, if you want God to either answer an oft-repeated prayer or release you from the strain of carrying it, or if you fit into one of an endless number of similar circumstances. . . . It's as if to say, 'God, I want You to know I'm very serious about this matter'" (*Praying More Effectively*, David C. Cook).

(As an exercise in seeing how this kind of intense prayer

effort works, try reading through the Book of Nehemiah.)

HABAKKUK—Habakkuk 1:2-4, 12, 13. Theme: the doubting heart. Principle: *Don't hesitate to bring your toughest questions to God*.

The Book of Habakkuk is a dramatic record of a man's angry questioning turning into a prayer of faith and praise. How can this happen? The key, when we doubt God's wisdom or motives, is to make sure that we are honestly seeking enlightenment from God. If we will let it, sincere doubt can push us and open us to new insights and changed perspectives. But to doubt with a closed mind—nursing the anger and confusion—only submerges the doubter deeper in rebellion, until that doubt eventually hardens into unbelief. Habakkuk's experience encourages us to come before God even at those times when we have little to bring besides our anger, fear, or doubt.

AN OUTSIDER—Matthew 15:21-28. Theme: prayer of desperation. Principle: *A desperate prayer is better than no prayer at all*.

It is true that some people only pray when they're desperate. But if you don't pray when your desperate, then you probably do very little praying at any other time at all! Here is a woman who must have known that Jesus was her only hope for her suffering daughter. She kept "crying out" after Jesus.

My wife, Carol, and I have come to the conclusion that Carol is a profound pray-er of "desperate prayers." We can smile now about the times over the years that she has literally fallen before the Lord and pounded the floor out of sheer desperation—and gotten immediate results! Because of this, sometimes I approach her (half humorously) with: "Honey, couldn't you just pray one of your 'desperate prayers' about this? I need an answer."

Particularly exquisite is our memory of her desperate prayer for children—after nine years of marriage, fertility testing, and adoption procedures. (We eventually had twins.) I believe God takes pleasure in knowing that He is the One we turn to when we are at the very end of the rope of our own resources.

PAUL: Ephesians 3:14-21. Theme: intercession for believers. Principle: *Our prayers ought to focus on the spiritual life of the Church and its members.*

Paul's prayers of intercession are a tremendous example of the kinds of concerns we can lift before the Lord on behalf of our brothers and sisters in Christ. Paul had the "big picture" in mind when he prayed. The following quote by Wentworth Pike (*Principles of Effective Prayer,* Prairie Bible Institute) points to the true emphasis of Biblical intercession:

GOOD POINT:

Spontaneity as opposed to formality in prayer has been stressed so much in evangelical circles that we have gone to the other extreme. Our prayers have degenerated into materialistic requests with very little spiritual content or concern for the glory of God. We have given so little attention to the words of our prayers that they are ineffective because they are non-specific: "Lord, bless the pastor and the Sunday School teachers, and bless the missionaries."

If we do get specific, we zero in on health, transportation, shelter, employment, and other practical concerns of daily life. Not that God is indifferent toward your need for a better car or the missionary's need for an airplane, but the New Testament prayers had a different emphasis.

Now, look back over this lesson. As you do, list several principles about prayer which you want to begin emphasizing more fully in your own prayer ministry.

_____

_____

_____

_____

Your Ministry of Prayer

Your Prayer Ministers Coordinator has been working especially hard this week, gathering information from your missionaries and other church-outreach ministries. This new information for prayer is included in the prayer list you will receive.

There are so many needs we can pray for as we think of our missionaries. Bill Wilson of the Overseas Missionary Fellowship suggests seven key areas:

1. Their personal and daily relationship to God through His Word, prayer, filling of the Spirit, maturity, victory and so forth.

2. For physical and emotional health.

3. For family relationships between husband and wife; for the children.

4. Ability to communicate fluently in the language and culture.

5. The ministry in which they are engaged. *Guidance + Power*

6. For their fellow workers.

7. For the country in which they serve.

If for any reason prayer fuel from your missionaries is not yet available, begin to compile your own list of prayer needs for missionaries, based on any facts you may know about them. You may use the form on page 123 for this purpose. We suggest including both home and foreign missionaries, as well as other ministries which your church either supports financially, or is a part of your ministry outreach.

10

PRAYING IN FAITH

During His earthly ministry, Jesus spoke a great deal about faith and prayer. He said on one occasion, "If that is how God clothes the grass of the field, which is here today and tomorrow is thrown into the fire, will he not much more clothe you, O you of *little faith*?" (Mt. 6:30). Of a Roman officer He said, "I tell you the truth, I have not found anyone in Israel with such *great faith*" (Mt. 8:10). And to His panicking disciples He said, "Why are you so afraid? Do you still have *no faith*?" (Mk. 4:40).

Trust in His care Faithful

God sear per peop of Fait

No fea

On another occasion, Jesus made this amazing statement: "I tell you the truth, if you have faith and do not doubt, not only can you do what was done to the fig tree, but also you can say to this mountain, 'Go, throw yourself into the sea,' and it will be done. If you believe, you will receive whatever you ask for in prayer" (Mt. 21:21, 22). And on still another occasion: "If you have *faith* as small as a mustard seed, you can say to this mulberry tree, 'Be uprooted and planted in the sea,' and it will obey you" (Lk. 17:6). Finally, "Jesus told his disciples a parable to show them that they should always pray and not give up." Then the text adds this challenging note: "However, when the Son of Man comes, will he find *faith* on the earth?" (Lk. 18:1, 8).

Your pow in praye

Faith scarce

How do you understand these words of Jesus? What

statement do they make to you about the part your faith
has in prayer?

*God is very concerned that I
have a faith in Him that
enables me to do exploits
for Him.*

Clearly, Jesus was challenging His disciples in the area
of their faith in relationship to prayer. His words served
both to rebuke, as well as to challenge these very human
followers of His. He calls His disciples even today, to
follow Him in the practice of believing prayer.

The Source of Faith

Salvation—the whole of it, including the very faith
needed to receive Christ—comes to us as God's gift: "For
it is by grace you have been saved, through faith—and this
not from yourselves, it is the gift of God" (Eph. 2:8).
Further, Jesus said, "No one can come to me unless the
Father who sent me draws him" (Jn. 6:44a). The initiative
comes from God. Just as He is the originator of our
physical life, so must He be of our spiritual life.

How do you respond to this truth?

*Encouraged to trust God for greater
challenges*

My heart says "I praise You; I thank You, Father. Thank
You for initiating spiritual life in me." Yet there is a human
side of this issue, too. Just as God has given man responsibility in regard to our physical life—whether we properly care for ourselves, eat properly, and so forth, He also
has given us responsibility in the area of our spiritual well-
being, including our walk of faith.

The Nature of Faith

Written to struggling Jewish Christians faced with incredible peer pressure and resulting persecution, the Book of Hebrews provides us with much help in understanding the nature of faith. Read the whole of Hebrews 11 before going on.

Being sure in verse 1 may also be translated "substance" (NASB margin). The word *certain* literally means "obtained a testimony" (NASB margin, vs. 2) and was used for the evidence which a lawyer gathers to win his case. Faith is like having sufficient evidence to win the object of its faith. While it is frequently said, "seeing is believing," the Word of God teaches just the opposite: "believing is seeing."

How would you describe faith, based on Hebrews 11:1?

A Lifestyle _Faith is living and acting as if the possible were reality._

Hebrews 11:3 can give us further help in understanding faith. Can you really understand *how* the physical universe was made out of something not visible? Though it may appear impossible, Scripture teaches us that it happened. Now think about this important key: As we receive this truth we begin to have faith in God.

Thinking about the nature of atomic energy may help strengthen our faith at this point. Just as the fission of atoms results in the release of enormous energy, *so the reverse must have occurred when God released His almighty power in creation!* Thus it was that the universe was created "at God's command" and not "out of what was visible."

Faith Is Essential _Trust in God to make something out of nothing._

The Old Testament prophet Habakkuk makes this ringing statement: *"The righteous will live by his faith"* (Hab. 2:4). This great Biblical statement reverberates again and again in the New Testament. For example, Paul, dealing in extreme firmness with the law-keeping Galatian believers, says, "Clearly no one is justified before God by the law, because"—quoting Habakkuk—" 'The righteous will live by faith' " (Gal. 3:11). As Paul proclaims the righteousness which is from God (Rom. 1:17), he declares that it is "a righteousness that is *by faith from first to last*," again quoting Habakkuk 2:4. From our first awareness and response to God—right through to our entering into glory—it is all through faith.

What do Hebrews 10:38 and 11:6, written to Christians under intense pressure and persecution, tell us about the importance of faith?

Unless you continue to have risky faith in God's ability + willingness to act He is not pleased with you.

How is this concept also expressed in Romans 8:18-25?

Faith is part of the game-plan Unseen/ perseverance/ hope

The Validation of Faith

Faith is illustrated in Hebrews 11 through a multitude of men and women from the Old Testament period.

How did Abel demonstrate his faith? (vs. 4)

Offering a sacrifice to God

How did Enoch express his? (vs. 5)

Pleased God by his faith

These two examples show that the writer is emphasizing that faith is expressed by actions. What two aspects of faith (see vs. 6) are essential in order to please God?

Belief in God + His nature Taking action in faith

The first of these aspects is relatively easy, since it is based on the abundant evidence for God's existence, seen in the world around us. (See Rom. 1:19-20 and Ps. 19.) Yet this is a genuine step of faith, for it involves believing in God whom we cannot see. The second step involves our lives—for those who believe on Christ commit themselves to following Him and doing His will.

Real Christian faith not only believes in God and confesses Christ as Savior, but also demonstrates this faith in an ongoing walk with Him.

What are some indications that you have this kind of faith?

_____

_____

_____

Verses 7-12 continue illustrating this kind of faith.

How did Noah demonstrate his faith, vs. 7?

Obeyed God when it had never rained before.

How did Abraham, in vss. 8-12?

Obeyed God to change his whole life.

And the examples in this great chapter on faith just go on and on. Note the stirring climactic account in verses 32-38. Tremendous victories of faith—including even the dead coming back to life.

The Test of Faith

But now glue your eyes to the second half of verse 35 and following. What do you find?

Some didn't get their answer in this life

In utter consternation we ask: Why this great difference? Why do some by faith walk through fire without harm—while others having the same faith, suffer being sawn in two? This is a hard question. But note this: On its answer hangs one of the most important lessons of faith. This answer is contained in Hebrews 11:13-16 and alluded to again in verses 39, 40. What is it?

I trust God because it links me with the eternal
where I will love Him.

God takes some of His children to the ultimate of faith's testing—after which there is nothing—not even life itself. But at its end, there is God, and the reward which He has promised (Heb. 11:6). The life of faith leads us on— through every circumstance—to this ultimate goal. (See also James 1:2-4 and I Peter 1:6-9.)

In the first verses of Hebrews 12 the Christian life is compared to that of a runner. In order to prepare for the race, the runner must lay aside everything that _encumbers_ as well as the _sin_ which easily besets him or her.

What are some things which hinder your running the race of faith?

Not only does this verse tell us *how* to prepare for the race of faith, but it also tells us how to continue in it. We are to run with _patience_ (see also Heb. 10:36). As in a physical race, it is not only important how we start, but also how we finish.

What helps you run your Christian race with endurance?

Remembering that God
is in charge. I'm pleasing Him.

Jesus looked past the suffering and shame of the Cross to the joy that was to be His (Heb. 12:2). We too, by faith, look past the suffering and shame we may experience in this life to the rewards God promises to His faithful followers.

Increasing Your Faith

The apostles said: "Increase our faith" (Lk. 17:5). What was Jesus' response to them? (in vs. 6)

It doesn't take much.

Apparently, it doesn't necessarily take mountain-sized faith to accomplish great things in the Kingdom. Yet most of us would gladly exchange the size of our faith for the mustard seed variety right now! Effective praying *does* require faith.

But how do we grow in faith? I can only speak from experience—looking back over my own life as a Christian and recalling the kinds of experiences that have served to strengthen my commitment to God and His will. Here, then, is what I have found so far:

FAITH INCREASES AS WE BECOME IMMERSED IN THE WORD. "Faith comes from hearing the message, and the message is heard through the word of Christ" (Rom. 10:17). Though raised in a Christian family, I didn't really start reading the Bible for myself until I left home and married. But once I started reading, a fire was sparked in my soul. I began taking a little New Testament to work and immersed myself in the gospels during lunch break. Getting intimately acquainted with the life and teachings of Jesus (and communing with His Spirit) caused my faith to grow by leaps and bounds!

Unfortunately, there have been periods in my life when the fire has cooled and I have let the place of Scripture meditation fall back in my list of priorities—to my loss. However, it rarely takes long for the barrenness of a purely self-directed life to cut through my neglect and draw me back to the Word of God and its values. "Your word is a lamp to my feet and a light for my path" (Ps. 119:105).

FAITH INCREASES AS WE GO THROUGH TRIALS. Looking back through my journal over the last five years, I am impressed with the intense praying, Scripture reading, and searching for God's guidance that took place during the tough times. But what really helps my faith grow is to look back and see that God really has led and provided even when circumstances looked quite threatening. Not that all my prayers were answered as I wanted them to be (thankfully!). But God's love and wisdom now seem to shine clearly through those hard times. As someone has said, God may not always lighten our burdens, but He will strengthen our backs.

Read I Peter 1:6-9. What is the ultimate purpose of a Christian's trials?

Refine Character

Be prepared to share with your group one of your own experiences with "gain through pain." Jot some notes here:

_____

_____

_____

FAITH INCREASES AS WE RISK COMMITMENT. During my seminary days, I faced a tough decision. I had to choose whether to remain where I was, in relative security and comfort, or to do what I sensed God was calling me to do—launch out on a rather scary new venture. I asked one of my professors for some advice about the decision. I said: "I feel like I want to hedge my bets." Her response was simply, "Gary, you just can't hedge your bets with God." I've never forgotten that, and I have yet to find it untrue. Real growth in faith happens when we put ourselves on the firing line—when following God means having everything to gain, but having something to lose, too. In short, to *have* faith means learning *to live by* faith. Abraham's experience in Genesis 22 is a good illustration.

We get a lot more out of own Christian life when we risk commitment.

According to Hebrews 11:32-38, Gideon, Barak, Samson, Jephthah, David, Samuel, the prophets, and many others were all called by God to enter into situations that were by no means safe, comfortable, or predictable. Yet they risked commitment—and they are, in God's eyes, faith heroes!

FAITH INCREASES THROUGH BEING WITH OTHER BELIEVERS. Fellowship and worship are essential ingredients of a growing faith. My own faith gets stronger when I meet with others and hear their accounts of how God has worked in their lives. I meet for worship and see fellow believers offering their love, time, and money to a God I can't see. Yet, as we all lift our souls in praise together, I am filled with a powerful new sense of the reality of His Kingdom.

There is another point about fellowship, too: We need to be intimately involved with others in order to be moved with compassion for them—coming to know their deep needs, and being moved to pray for them. Richard Foster (*Celebration of Discipline*, Harper and Row) said: "We do not pray for people as 'things' but as 'persons' whom we love. If we have God-given compassion and concern for others, our faith will grow and strengthen as we pray."

Ultimately, praying in faith means knowing God's promises and not doubting that God will act—though we do not know *how* or *when*. This is based upon our firm conviction that God is holy, good, and *has our best interests at heart*. In fact, our faith can survive any trial or crisis as long as it can rest in that one great truth: *We are loved unconditionally.*

If you are immersing yourself in the Word, seeking to rejoice in the midst of trials, risking commitment to God's cause in specific life decisions, and meeting regularly with others for fellowship and worship, then be assured: Your faith is increasing and your prayers are having an effect.

Using the Faith Key

A striking illustration of the ministry of faith in prayer is found in the account of Jesus' interaction with a father who's son suffered from convulsions. You can read about this in Mark 9:14-24. How did Jesus challenge this father?

_____

How would you identify with the father's response, vs. 24?

_____

Now look up two additional references and choose one to "chew" on: Hebrews 11:6; James 1:5-7. How will this verse challenge and inspire your prayers this week?

_____

_____

Your Ministry of Prayer

This week, in addition to the requests you are praying about from your church, from your missionaries, and from your denomination, you should also receive requests from your PMC relating to regional, national and international concerns. While providing this list of requests is the responsibility of your PMC, you may also compile a list on your own. Much fuel for prayer can come directly from your newspaper, or radio/TV set. These prayer requests should focus especially on issues having a spiritual significance, that is those issues which you perceive as affecting the Kingdom of God.

If you choose to do so, you may make a copy of page 124 of this workbook and record these requests there.

Concerning prayer for government, we have a clear mandate. The apostle Paul says:

I urge, then, first of all, that requests, prayers, intercession and thanksgiving be made for everyone—for kings and all those in authority—I Timothy 2:1, 2.

11

PRAYING
WITH AUTHORITY

At a conference of missionaries and Chinese pastors held shortly before the Communists gained control of China, one pastor gave a striking address. He said he and his colleagues were more than grateful to those who had brought them the Word of life and the Gospel of Christ. But there was one thing more that they should teach their spiritual children. This new thing was how to pray with authority, so that they might know how to take their stand before the throne of God and rebuke the forces of evil, hold steady, and gain the victory.

The need of teaching on this aspect of prayer is no less pressing in Western lands than in the East. Too few Christians progress from mere presentation of petitions to God into the area of the spiritual warfare of which Paul speaks in Ephesians 6:10-18.
—J. O. Sanders, *Prayer Power Unlimited*

Turn to Ephesians 6. How would you describe the nature of the believer's warfare, based on verses 10-12?

A battle engaged in from a position of strength

It is vital that we see Christian life and ministry in light of what Paul calls our struggle against rulers, authorities, powers, and spiritual forces of evil. We will be tempted in myriad ways to allow these forces to thwart God's work through us as individuals and as the corporate body of Christ. As an example, consider governmental powers that promote practices of racial or economic discrimination. In what ways can Christians take their stand against such "schemes"?

Write letters to appropriate authorities.

Prayer as an offensive action.

assertiveness

total Warfare takes aggression, compassion

On the personal level, what are some temptations you experience, as "flaming arrows," that try to keep you from seeking God's will?

need a new sense accounta- ty and tivation.

Disengage b/c of God's sovereignty.

"Sit down young man, when God wants to save the heathen He'll do it w/o your help."

What resources has God given, according to Ephesians 6, to enable you to win in this struggle against satanic influences?

Truth, Righteousness,

Faith, Salvation, Word, Prayer

How does the Christian "put on" these resources?

We were given these at conversion, it is necessary to let them flow through us in daily living.

How do you understand prayer (vs. 18) fitting into this picture of spiritual resources?

The whole thing is bathed & empowered by prayer.

Pray in the Spirit

This command occurs in just these words only once in Scripture, although the idea contained in them may be said to occur frequently. It is therefore important for us to learn just what is meant and how we can practice this kind of praying.

What relationship do you see between putting on the spiritual armor, and praying "in the Spirit"? Describe this relationship. *Involves:*

1) living & abiding in His presence (ungrieved, filled).
2) Pray by means of & in dependence on His help
3) This kind of praying involves warfare.
(struggle, effort, work)

But just how do we pray "in the Spirit"? This is not an easy question, but reflect on Romans 8:26, 27. What key truth is revealed here? How can we implement it?

Praying "in the Spirit" = prayer under His control, moving in the direction of His will, sanctioned by the presence of His transforming power. Praying in the Spirit is more God's ... than ... Properly motivated and well-intentioned prayer not ... the ... of God will ... work.

H.C.G. Moule, noting that the term occurs without the definite article (thus literally translated, "in spirit") says that it means surrounded by His presence and power. J. O. Sanders (*Prayer Power Unlimited*) amplifies this thought, saying:

It is clear that praying in the Spirit means much more than praying by the Spirit's help, although that is included. We pray by means of and in dependence on the Spirit's help, but the Spirit is the atmosphere in which the believer lives. So long as He is ungrieved, He is able to guide us in our petitions and create in us the faith that claims the answer. Our prayers will then be in substance the same as the intercessions of the Spirit within.

Reflect again on Ephesians 6:18, 19 in the context of the believer's spiritual armor. How can you successfully implement this on a practical level in your prayer ministry?

The battle must be bathed in persevering prayer.
Holiness   Influence   Parenting   Faith
Purity   Growth   Temptation

In one sense, we approach the Christian life with great confidence, including the ministry of prayer. The victory *is* ours—for we are in Christ Jesus who has given us all the resources for victory. Christ assures this from His position at the right hand of the Father, where He also intercedes for us. Yet in a very real sense there is an ongoing spiritual battle raging. The victory is not *automatic*. Our part is crucial. Our ministry often involves struggle, effort, and work.

Look at Colossians 2:1 and its context. How does Paul describe his ministry, especially for those he has never seen?

Great Struggle (taking on opposing
forces a schemes)
Arduous labor

A further glimpse of how these early ministers prayed is found in Colossians 4:12 and 13.

What was the objective of Epaphras' praying?

For their spiritual formation into
maturity & confidence in the will of God.

How would you go about praying like him?

Labor earnestly for them
in prayer.

Authoritative praying must be praying that comes to grips with the realities of the spiritual battles involved. These realities were clear to those who prayed in the New Testament. They must be equally clear to us today.

Pray in Jesus' Name

Authoritative praying must also involve praying in Jesus' name. Jesus made this abundantly clear as He prepared to leave His disciples and return to Heaven.

Jesus said, "I will do whatever you ask *in my name*, so that the Son may bring glory to the Father. You may ask me for anything *in my name*, and I will do it" (Jn. 14:13, 14). "Then the Father will give you whatever you ask *in my name*," He said in John 15:16. Again, "I tell you the truth, my Father will give you whatever you ask *in my name*. Until now you have not asked for anything *in my name*. Ask and you will receive, and your joy will be complete . . . . In that day you will ask *in my name*" (Jn. 16:23, 24, 26).

Are we asking in Jesus' name? What does this mean? Is it simply saying the words? Certainly, we would agree, it is *not* just saying the words. But what does it really mean? And why did Jesus put such emphasis on prayer in His name?

When Jesus spoke these words He was nearing the end of His earthly ministry. The Garden of Gethsemane was just ahead. The Crucifixion was near. "I am going to the Father," Jesus told His disciples, "and I will do whatever you ask in my name, so that the Son may bring glory to the Father" (Jn. 14:12, 13). Jesus was teaching them a final lesson on prayer. Before this time, the disciples had made many requests directly to Jesus. Now He was saying that this approach would soon no longer be possible. "I am not saying that I will ask the Father on your behalf," He told them. Rather, they were now to ask the Father directly—"in my name," Jesus said.

To help us understand the meaning of this command, *Authority* reflect on Matthew 28:18-20. Summarize your thoughts below.

v.18 Authority - power or right to command, act, enforce obedience, or make final decisions (Jurisdiction) Call the shots! v.19 Authorization — power delegated to another "You have all authority to act."

The significance of using Jesus' name also involves His *but only* character; His very person. Can we conceive of asking in *to fulfill* Jesus' name for things that would violate His character? *His orders.* Or things that would not be consistent with His cause in this world? Hardly.

To use Jesus' name in prayer is to use His authority within the confines of His character and will. Christ is in us; we are His Body on earth. He has promised that He would build His church, and that the gates of Hades

106

would not prevail against it. Even now—through you and me—He is seeking to continue building His Church. His authority—the authority He exercised on earth—is our authority today. Authority to ask anything "in His name." An awesome thought, with awesome power.

Summarize your understanding of what it means to pray "in Jesus' name."

To use His authority w/in the confines of His character + His will to move reality toward His purposes.

Pray According to God's Will

Praying with the authority of Jesus' name must also mean that our prayers are in accord with the will of God. This is not the same as merely praying for things we think God will do anyway. Nor does this kind of praying seek to "get God to do things"—as though to manipulate Him. Rather, it means seeking to pray for those things that are within the moral, ethical, and spiritual will of God. True prayer finds itself in the flow of what God is doing in the world. It seeks His pleasure. _To fit into His plan not to alter His plan._

The clearest example of praying according to the will of God is doubtless found in the life of our Lord Himself. To find this we will look for Jesus in Gethsemane, where He prayed, "My Father, if it is possible, may this cup be taken from me" (Matthew 26:39). If there was ever a prayer that He desired to have answered, it was this one. Every part of His human nature cried out for deliverance. The Cross and the agony of death loomed before Him.

How often did Jesus pray this way? (Mt. 26:44) _3 X_

With what result? _He drank it._

In that moment of extreme agony Jesus was able to pray, "Yet not as I will, but as you will." Even the Lord Jesus had to experience the surrender of His own will to that of the Father.

What application do you see of this principle to your prayer ministry?

Be always ready to yield to His authority.

True prayer is that which desires alignment with the will of God. What is our assurance as we approach God in prayer? (I Jn. 5:14, 15)

He will give us what we ask for when aligned w/ His will.

This being the case, how can we be guided in God's will as we pray? The following guideline questions may help us.

1. Is the prayer in accord with Scripture? Obviously, requests not aligned with God's Word cannot be God's will. This principle of guidance means for me that:

3 X for release from trial (Jesus & Paul)
Focus needs to change from how do I get out of this to How do I get thru this.

objective
subject

2. Have circumstances guided in the direction of this request? Read I Corinthians 16:5-9. In verse 9, Paul mentions two aspects of his circumstances: a "great door," and significant opposition.

What appears to have been his interpretation of these circumstances in relation to his plans?

This indicated that God wanted him there. opposition – lost sheep attract birds

Needs ← → Pretenders. profiteers. False profits

3. Sometimes special, even remarkable circumstances can be involved. What special circumstance guided Paul in Acts 16:6-10, and with what results?

God communicated His specific will to Paul thru a vision.
Paul changed course & went out under God's authority.

4. Would the answer to this prayer demonstrate God's love in action? (See I Jn. 3:21, 22.)

_____

5. What is the counsel of other Christians, especially those who are "over you in the Lord"? (I Thess. 5:12)

_____*Seek Counsel*_____

6. Has God laid this burden on your heart? Having such a burden is often an indication that God desires to work, in response to your prayers for this matter.

_____

Having satisfied yourself on these points, you may need to continue in persevering prayer until the answer is received.

Your Ministry of Prayer

As you near the end of this course, we want your prayer ministry to continue on with God's blessing. This week make some plans for how you and your team of prayer ministers will carry on your prayer ministry after this course is completed. Be prepared to talk this over and make your plans as a group. Here are a few suggestions.

1. Plan a monthly fellowship meeting for inspiration, request updates, and a prayer time. You may even choose Lesson 12 in this course to be completed during the first of these monthly meetings. How about a potluck supper?

2. Select a prayer partner with whom you will share weekly. This can be done at a time when you can meet together, or by telephone.

3. Participate in the regular church prayer meetings, where you may share key requests and in other ways have opportunity to encourage the ministry of prayer.

There are two sides to my salvation
This I did. — what I am in myself — this I despise.
This He did — what I am in Christ — This I glory in
It is an affront to God to downplay either reality

4. Ask your pastor to share about this ministry at least quarterly, in the church bulletin or from the pulpit.

As you meet together this week, work out your plans for group activities which will strengthen and encourage your ongoing ministry of prayer into the future. Write out these plans below.

Proper Self-esteem a self-respect comes not from an inflated view of me but from a biblical view of what God has done in me.

One more suggestion: Offer this LAMP course, _Your Ministry of Prayer_, frequently, to recruit additional people to become involved in this crucial ministry.

The "worm" concept

1. Not only is there danger of pride regarding spiritual + personal progress + attainment, but there is also a danger of pride in my evaluation of my personal depravity.

2. I glorify God <u>best</u> when I fully acknowledge <u>both</u>

   A) The depth of my depravity + its reality in my life. and

   B) the awesome glory + reality of the new creation that God has made, is making ultimately will make of — child of Satan - Child of God — Kingdom of darkness - Kingdom of Light.

Biblical self-esteem / Self love / Self Respect — basis for that earned but given

All by God's work

2 Cor 5:17 I am now something significantly, substantially and eternally different than what I... (done when?) Reconciled to God — enemy to friend
Divine Nature — Indwelling Spirit — Able now t...

12

BEING A PRAYER MINISTER

*Little Jim wanted to play football. His heart was set on becoming a professional player. "I'm smart enough to do it," he thought to himself. Actually, Jim was quite a bookworm. He read all the time and knew exactly what to do to become a famous football star— or so he thought. "I'll check out some books from the library and find out everything about this game," he said to his younger sister on their way to school. Several weeks later the first day of tryouts came. After warm-up exercises, the coach shouted, "Tackle practice!" When Jim reached the front of the line, he scrambled for the boy with the ball, but to no avail. Once, twice, three times the runner easily avoided Jim's frantic attempts to bring him down. Finally, the coach called Jim off to the side. "Jim," he whispered, "I just don't think you're cut out for football." "Oh yes I am," he retorted. "Ask me anything about the game. I know the answer to any question you can ask." The coach knelt down and put his hand on Jim's oversized shoulder pad. "Jim, in football it's not what you **know**. It's what you **do** that counts."*

—Richard Pratt in *Pray With Your Eyes Open* (Presbyterian and Reformed Publishing Co.)

The lesson Jim learned about the bottom line in football is the same kind of lesson that will keep nudging at us as we attempt greater involvement with prayer: Is it going to be what we *know* about prayer, or what we *do* about it?

Surely it is the will of God that we launch ourselves into a life-long ministry of praying—not just for our own needs, but for the needs of others as well. And without question, prayer is one of the greatest needs of the church today— the kind of praying Jesus taught and practiced in the gospels; praying that the apostles and other disciples practiced, and as a result saw the mighty hand of God at work; praying that will advance His Kingdom in our world.

A lot of that kind of praying *is* taking place in our world. But why isn't it happening on a broader scale? The mirror in Isaiah 59 identifies one reason in the life of the ancient Israelites:

> *Surely the arm of the Lord is not too short to save, nor his ear too dull to hear.... Your iniquities have separated you from your God; your sins have hidden his face from you, so that he will not hear...* (Isa. 59:1, 2).

Israel's ongoing sin had eventually alienated them from the God who loved them deeply. But the message doesn't end there. Look at these shocking words: *He was appalled that there was no one to intercede.*

No one to intercede? In a nation of God-chosen, God-blessed people, there was *no one* to intercede? This tragic truth was to bear its own kind of fruit. The Israelites reaped the destructive consequences of their attitudes and brought down judgment upon themselves—leaving only a remnant to survive, and that in exile.

Bob Samms, founder and director of LAMP, and former missionary to the Philippines, challenges us with these words:

> *Dear fellow-pilgrims in the ministry of prayer: Circumstances are substantially the same in our land today. The gross, the vile, the abominable sin of whatever name—is everywhere in gaudy apparel. It has thrust its vile hands into virtually every part of our society, even the privacy of our homes and personal*

Not because of what I have done, but b/c of what He has done to me x in me □ this dirty rag can now be a c...

lives. *The unwary and deceived are clutched in the embrace of sin—being dragged down to the very brink of hell itself, stayed only by the long-suffering hand of God—while He looks about for intercessors.*

The question we must face is this: Will He find true intercessors in our day of such great need? Millions are arriving on that brink—to a Christ-less grave. Will He still—after all the lessons we have learned, after all the history we have witnessed, after all the knowledge of Scripture we have—be "appalled that there was no one to intercede"?

Your Ministry of Prayer

A call to prayer ministry cannot be responded to lightly. Becoming an effective prayer minister may require further prioritizing of our time and energies. It will require personal discipline in following through with our commitment. It will also require the support of our church and the active ministry of thePrayer Ministers Coordinator to compile and send out prayer requests regularly. And it will also involve an ongoing group accountability and support structure.

TIME MANAGEMENT FOR PRAYER. During the past 12 weeks you have spent perhaps an hour preparing each lesson. The weekly class and travel time has cost you additional hours weekly. You have also been spending time in prayer daily.

The total amount of time weekly, on an average, that I have spent daily in prayer and in connection with this course on prayer is _____.

How much time, on an average, do you feel you could commit to spending in prayer daily for His Kingdom purposes in the world? For some of us taking this course, who are very busy, perhaps 15 minutes daily would be a good goal to set. For others of us that God may be calling to a very special ministry of prayer, this could well be one

1 of holy blessing to someone— that is
self-esteem

hour daily, or even more. Whatever the amount, write down below the amount you feel is realistic in your situation.

"With God's help I will commit myself to _____ minutes/hours daily in prayer."

While you may not achieve this full amount of prayer time each day, it is nevertheless important to set a specific goal for yourself.

The next step is to "talk to yourself." How am I going to achieve this goal? We're not talking here about the content of prayers, but rather planning the time to make it happen. What things need to change in my daily life-style in order to achieve it? What about the time now spent reading the morning paper? Watching TV? Scheduling this time for prayer may also affect my time of retiring in the evening, and possibly other regular or infrequent activities. The question is, what priority level in my daily activities am I going to give to prayer?

Realistically, the things I will change in order to fulfill my high-priority prayer commitment include:

_____

_____

I plan to do this by:

_____

_____

_____

_____

ORGANIZING FOR ONGOING MINISTRY. While in earlier lessons you worked on getting prayer information, now is the time to make sure that everything is working smoothly. Is your present arrangement effective for your receiving

114

prayer requests weekly? Take whatever time is needed during your group session this week to make sure that these plans are firm and will work.

Now is the time to make a commitment check on your hard-working PMC (Prayer Ministers Coordinator). Are there any problems that he or she has encountered? Clearly, this is a large commitment on this person's time. Yet this job is crucial to the flow of prayer information to each of you. Write below anything you see that might need to be discussed during the next group meeting.

_____

_____

_____

Is your PMC seriously overworked? If so, how about dividing his or her responsibilities? For example, someone else might handle just the letters from missionaries. Another person might handle the requests from your denomination and other church-related ministries. If there is a need to divide the work, discuss this and make your plans accordingly.

If your church has a computer, the assembly and distribution of this information can be significantly expedited. In this case, the church office can set up a prayer request bank, where all prayer request information is stored. Divide this up into the several categories you have selected, and begin inputting this information. Once a week, copies of the current lists of prayer requests should be copied for each prayer minister.

Plan "B"

Hopefully everything is going smoothly and you are involved in an effective ministry of prayer. However, just in case things have not gone that well, let's review what is needed to make it work.

REQUESTS FROM YOUR CHURCH. Praying for the needs of your own church should be a primary part of your prayer ministry. Some of these requests will represent regular, ongoing requests, such as prayer for your pastor, church staff, regular meetings, your church outreach ministries, and so forth. Other requests coming from your church will be special requests, and perhaps some which are of a confidential nature. You will need to work out a plan to handle these requests.

REQUESTS FROM YOUR DENOMINATION. In many cases your denomination or church group will provide prayer requests for you to pray for. Sometimes a prayer sheet is available on request. Or such requests may be printed in your denominational periodical. In other cases a "prayer request hotline" is available for your use.

The sources of denominational information on prayer with which I am familiar include (provide name, address, etc. if it is known to you):

_____

_____

_____

REQUESTS FROM YOUR MISSIONARIES. The greatest of all missionaries wrote: "Brothers, pray for us that the message of the Lord may spread rapidly and be honored" (II Thess. 3:1). Prayer for missionaries is obviously a vital need. The question remains: How can we do so effectively? Some suggestions follow:

1. Pray for missionaries you know, support, and love. Your church should be on their regular prayer letter list.

2. Write your missionaries and ask for prayer requests they might not want to include in a more public letter. Make sure they know that this information is for private circulation only among your prayer ministers.

3. Your prayer coordinator may be able to find key information from their mission or other mission agencies which will provide a wider scope of strategic prayer fuel.

This information should be digested, collated, and added to your bank of prayer information.

REQUESTS FOR YOUR NATION. We already know that we are called to pray for "kings and all that are in authority" (I Timothy 2:2). This certainly means the highest officials of our land, as well as those locally. It surely includes the great moral and ethical issues of our day. It ought to include as well, specific issues that involve the work of God's Kingdom on earth.

Information that can help you pray for national concerns include:

THE NAE INSIGHT (National Association of Evangelicals)— P.O. Box 28, Wheaton, IL 60189.

NATIONAL AND INTERNATIONAL RELIGION REPORT—P.O. Box 21433, Roanoke VA 24018.

REPORT FROM THE CAPITOL (Baptist Joint Committee for Public Affairs)—200 Maryland Ave., N.E., Washington, DC 20002.

CHURCH AND STATE—8102 Fenton St., Silver Springs, MD 20910.

E.S.A. ADVOCATE (Evangelicals for Social Action)—5107 Newhall St., Philadelphia, PA 19144.

These sources of information, plus praying for your own family, neighborhood, and personal ministry will provide a great source of vital prayer fuel.

Devote yourselves to prayer, being watchful and thankful. And pray for us, too, that God may open a door for our message, so that we may proclaim the mystery of Christ. . . . Pray that I may proclaim it clearly, as I should. Colossians 4:2-4

Daily Prayer Requests:

From your Monday through Saturday lists, list key requests you want to pray for daily.

Date	Concern	Answer

Monday Focus: CHURCH

*I pray that out of his glorious riches he may strengthen you
with power through his Spirit in your inner being, so that Christ
may dwell in your hearts through faith. And I pray that you,
being rooted and established in love, may have power, together
with all the saints, to grasp how wide and long and high and deep
is the love of Christ, and to know this love that surpasses
knowledge—that you may be filled to the measure of all the
fullness of God* (Eph. 3:16-19).

Areas for Prayer

For the goals and ministry direction of the church; for
the various aspects of the pastor's ministry; for the responsibilities and relationships of staff; for the ministry of
equipping believers for service; for evangelism and outreach in the community; for financial provision and ministry though giving; for special needs of which I am aware;
for my areas of ministry at church; for "prayer chain"
requests or requests provided by the church.

My Prayer Concerns

Date	Concern	Answer

Tuesday Focus: PERSONAL MINISTRY

You are the light of the world. A city on a hill cannot be hidden. Neither do people light a lamp and put it under a bowl. Instead they put it on its stand, and it gives light to everyone in the house. In the same way, let your light shine before men, that they may see your good deeds and praise your Father in heaven (Mt. 5:14-16).

Areas for Prayer

For neighbors—for opportunities to serve them; for special needs they may have; for opportunities to share Christ with them; for opportunities to model a Christian life-style before them. For friends—their needs, spiritual and material; opportunities to help them and to share Christ with them. For other areas of personal ministry.

My Prayer Concerns

Date	Concern	Answer

Wednesday Focus: WORK

They could find no corruption in him, because he was trustworthy and neither corrupt nor negligent (Dan. 6:4b).

Do you see a man skilled in his work? He will serve before kings; he will not serve before obscure men (Prov. 22:29).

Areas for Prayer

For skill and competence in my area of work; for relationships with my supervisor and other workers; for the spiritual and material needs of my fellow-workers; for opportunities to share my faith; for personal attitudes and actions which will allow Christ to more effectively shine through me; for direction in my profession and employment; for opportunities to share my faith on the job.

My Prayer Concerns

Date	Concern	Answer

Thursday Focus: FAMILY

Early in the morning [Job] would sacrifice a burnt offering for each of [his children] (Job 1:5).

Areas for Prayer

For my spouse—the quality of our relationships; work responsibilities; decisions; health; etc. For our children—for their spiritual birth; for their continuing growth in Christ; for their physical and emotional needs; for quality time and relationships with them; for their relationships and activities at church; for their school circumstances and relationships; for their special activities and needs. For the needs of other relatives.

My Prayer Concerns

Date	Concern	Answer

Friday Focus: MISSIONS

The harvest is plentiful but the workers are few. Ask the Lord the harvest, therefore, to send out workers into his harvest field (Mt. 9:37, 38).

And pray for us, too, that God may open a door for our message.... Pray that I may proclaim it clearly, as I should (Col. 4:3, 4).

Areas for Prayer

For planning missionary strategy and work; for nationals' salvation and Christian growth; for training of nationals and their leadership roles; for financial and ministry related needs; for physical and emotional needs.

My Prayer Concerns

Date	Concern	Answer

Saturday Focus: GOVERNMENT

If my people, who are called by my name, will humble themselves and pray and seek my face and turn from their wicked ways, then will I hear from heaven and will forgive their sin and will heal their land (II Chron. 7:14).

I urge, then, first of all, that requests, prayers, intercession and thanksgiving be made for everyone—for kings and all those in authority, that we may live peaceful and quiet lives in all godliness and holiness (I Tim. 2:1, 2).

Areas for Prayer

For officials in government—the President; Vice-President; members of Congress; the Supreme Court Justices; state and local politicians. For issues of great moral and spiritual concern—widespread substance abuse; moral degeneration; abortion on demand; destruction of family life; etc. For political events—national and local elections; for peace; for moral and ethical causes. For special concerns world-wide.

My Prayer Concerns

Date	Concern	Answer

LESSON
PLANS

Notes to the Leader

• Look through all of the lesson plans in advance to note places where advanced preparation is needed, or materials must be gotten well before the class session. That way you won't be caught off guard.

• Try to include in all your group sessions some of the key ingredients for building group life: a time for sharing, a time for prayer, and perhaps light refreshments around which significant conversation can take place. These LAMP study groups should be much more than just an intellectual trip. They can become the means of a changed lifestyle and a launching pad to more effective service. They can also become a means of developing strong bonds of Christian fellowship.

• Have an informal Introductory Meeting before jumping right into the study. This meeting should include: plenty of time to get acquainted with each other, time to hand out the books and give clear instructions about what will be expected each week.

• Be sure to have an "accountability period" within each class session, at the very beginning of the class. The workbook has a series of ongoing assignments to be checked on week by week as the group progresses through the course.

• The following two activities should be done each week—EVEN THOUGH THEY WILL NOT BE MENTIONED EACH TIME IN THE SPECIFIC LESSON PLANS:

       1) send a group prayer notebook around the group

at the beginning of each class so group members can add praises and requests to be shared at the close of the study; 2) To close each "Discovery in the Word" section, always ask for any questions/observations/sharing from the workbook assignment during the week, and go over the answers to the written questions in the chapter.

Lesson 1

ACCOUNTABILITY: Check on whether everyone was able to fulfill the first requirement of the course: obtaining a ring-binder prayer notebook.

FOCUS: Contact a group member to do a short demonstration of a special tool or instrument he or she uses at work—explaining its inner workings. Then have learners share about a time in their lives when they may have gotten sudden insight into the true nature of a situation—discovering what happened behind the scenes. From this activity move into a brief explanation about the "behind the scenes" reality of our Christian existence—the Kingdom.

DISCOVER: Read aloud Romans 8:18-25 and zero in on the workbook question: "What is the greatest challenge to the spread of the Kingdom in the world today?" Encourage participants to first focus on community, national and global issues, then bring it right down to where they live— What is the challenge at their work, home, school?

Emphasize that one's total life-style influences the spread of the Kingdom by focusing in on the imagery of II Cor. 2:14-16. On chalkboard or newsprint make a two-column list with the headings: "Aroma" and "Kingdom Living Applications." As a group, fill in some general characteristics under "Aroma" such as: pervades, influences, attracts, repels, etc. Then fill in the second column to bring out practical ways we really are the "aroma of Christ in the world."

Then share answers to the last three questions under

"Prayer in the Church," making sure that this point comes through: *Working at a prayer ministry means constant maturing in Christian life-style as well, since that life-style is the context out of which the ministry grows.*

RESPOND: Divide into sharing groups of 3 or 4 people. Have the members of each group take turns completing the following two sentences:
1) "The big thing I'm hoping to gain from this course is_____."
2) "If I had to name one thing that might hinder me from accomplishing this it would be _____
_____."

Close with prayer.

RECAP: Give a quick a reminder about 1) preparing to select the Prayer Ministers Coordinator during the third group session; and 2) a word about getting started on their prayer journals and daily prayer time, this week. Offer to explain further, or help any individual who would like to talk with you after the class session.

Lesson 2

ACCOUNTABILITY: Check on each individual's progress with regard to purchasing a prayer notebook. Their task is to purchase the notebook, organize it, and begin making daily entries.

FOCUS: Begin with a focus on the "gearing up" theme. Briefly interview one or two campers (or travelers) in the group about their preparations for making a trip: What things do you do before starting out? What needs to be gathered and gotten ready? (There could even be some humorous anecdotes about things that were *forgotten*!)
Then ask the group: "Share about a time when you wished you hadn't neglected to 'gear up' first . . . ."

DISCOVER: Go to "The How" section under "Three Practical

Matters" for your Discovery time: First, ask learners to share their responses to the following comments concerning Matthew 6:5-8:

The Pharisees had made prayer into a public performance to demonstrate their "righteousness." The "reward" was to be whatever meager amount of praise or respect they could get from those who saw them.

But prayer is best done in private, as a child conversing with his father, in simple honesty. We can be as candid as possible about our needs and spiritual condition.

God knows our needs, but He calls us to make ourselves known to Him—to open up. In other words, God desires **intimacy**.

Now ask someone to share his or her response to Acts 17:24-28. Then share the following comment:

God is close, immanent. We do not have to *struggle* to get God's attention. The real struggle is making time to pray, and then praying *honestly*.

Now ask for responses to Romans 8:13-17. Then share the following comment:

All prayer (indeed, every Christian "work") is motivated and empowered by the Spirit. To be indwelt and controlled by the Holy Spirit is to be related to God by spiritual adoption as a son (daughter). It is a great privilege to be able to call God "Father." And it means we can approach him *conversationally*.

Let those who wish to, share some of their responses to the ACTS exercise in their workbook. If they share prayer requests (supplication), be sure to jot these down and remember them for group prayer at the close of the session.

RESPOND: Spend plenty of time here with the practical matters of the learners' prayer time and journals. Explain and clarify in detail the three requirements that are summarized under "Your Ministry of Prayer," and discuss ways to help one another follow through. After a time of mutual encouragement, close the class session with prayer.

RECAP: Briefly remind the group that in the next group session they will be selecting their Prayer Ministers Coordinator. Ask them to be in prayer about this important decision.

Lesson 3

ACCOUNTABILITY: During the week preceding this session group members were asked to continue developing their list of daily prayer requests. How are group members doing on this? Does anyone want to share how it's going? Any obstacles? Advice?

Also take the necessary amount of time now to select your Prayer Ministers Coordinator. Take as much time as needed to thoroughly review the PMC's "job description" and get this person launched into this ministry.

FOCUS: Begin by looking at the concept of "name." Let each group member give a brief account of their family name derivation (perhaps some ethnic/genealogical history). Then say: "Our names say something about who we are, where we are from, the family that has shaped us. In the same way, knowing God's name(s) is a way for us to get a clearer picture of who God is."

DISCOVER: Have learners spend time sharing their responses to the "why it makes impact" and "affect" sections under the three attributes of God that they chose to focus on.

Sum up by discussing these questions:

1. In what ways has your concept of God been broadened by a closer look at the names and attributes of God in this lesson?

2. In thinking about your friends, neighbors, co-workers, what would you say are the most "typical" ways of thinking about God?

3. How can our public life and witness make a difference in how people around us view God? Be specific.

4. Share any insights you may have gained from the author's discussion of the three attributes: omniscience, sovereignty, goodness.

RESPOND: You may choose to use this week's response time to do a Group Check. Look at the dynamics of what's happening in the group now and over the last few weeks. How are people feeling about the course so far? About their relationships with one another? About the structure of the class time? Other concerns?

RECAP: Briefly remind the group that this week the Prayer Ministers Coordinator should be providing them with their first weekly list of prayer requests from the church.

Lesson 4

ACCOUNTABILITY: Last week the group should have finalized plans for getting prayer request information to each member weekly. Has that been done? Has the Prayer Ministers Coordinator been chosen? Is he/she clear about the nature of this ministry and what it will require?

FOCUS: For about two minutes, do a "complimenting game": have everyone converse with his neighbor, saying nothing but good things about that person. Then ask: "How did it feel to be so *praised*?" After some sharing, explain that human complimenting can quickly degenerate into a flattery session. But God is worthy of, and *deserves*, every bit of praise we can offer Him!

Now ask individuals to choose a private place in the room or building to spend 3 minutes in silent praise, *complimenting God*. When you come together after the 3 minutes, discuss: "Was it hard to spend three minutes in complimenting God? Why or why not? Did anyone run out of things to say?"

From this discussion, move into a look at how Jesus approached His Heavenly Father . . . .

DISCOVER: Have learners look up and read the passages about how Jesus addressed God the Father. Discuss: "How can we apply the example of Jesus?"

Then focus on John 4:23, and the fact that God *desires* our worship. Ask: "What is true worship?" Three points that should come out are:
- the idea of *attributing worth to God;*
- speaking *to* God rather than *about* God;
- true worship is motivated by God Himself
(I Pet. 4:11).

Ask: "Why do you believe the author stresses the second point above?" (Because it's the difference between discussing theology and relating personally to God.)

Give opportunity for learners to share (specifically) how they have found worship to satisfy them in one of the three ways stated under "Worship Satisfies the Soul":
- we get our perspective back
- we are led to repentance and renewal
- we fulfill our created purpose

RESPOND: The best way to end this class session would be to spend a few moments in corporate worship. Choose one of the worship "suggestions" given in the workbook.

RECAP: Briefly remind the group that in the week ahead they should be focusing on requests for their personal ministry—involving neighbors, friends, people at work, etc. A special form for recording these requests is provided on page 120 of the workbook.

Lesson 5

ACCOUNTABILITY: During the week preceding this session group members were to focus on requests for their personal ministry with neighbors, friends, work associates, etc. Have they developed such a list? Did they use the form on page 120 of the workbook? How are they doing with their personal prayer times?

FOCUS: Write the following on newsprint or chalkboard: **"When the commandment came, sin sprang to life" (Rom. 7:9).** Say: "Let's think about ways we may have seen this principle work itself out in our daily lives. What examples do you have in your own life of feeling a rule or a law "push" you toward sin?"

DISCOVER: Say: "Let's look more closely at the apostle Paul's struggle with the power of sin to see what insight we can gain for our own struggles." Have someone read aloud Romans 7:14-25. Then share answers to the first three questions under "Keeping the Path Clear."

Focus heavily on question #3 about the positive side of the passage in 7:25. Then relate this to Romans 8:1-4 (which expands upon vs. 25). Briefly summarize the meaning of this passage.

Ask those who are willing to tell what their major prayer "hindrance" is. Write these on a chalkboard, then go to the Scriptures under "It's Worth it." Assign a different one of these passages to groups of 2 or 3 and ask them to answer the question: "How does this passage give encouragement to overcome the hindrances?" Re-gather and share the groups' insights.

Now move to specific applications of overcoming strategies under the Response section below.

RESPOND: Spend the last portion of your class time focusing in on the two questions that immediately precede "It's Worth It." These questions asked your group members 1) to come up with specific strategies to start overcoming their hindrances to regular prayer; and 2) to share their plans with the group—getting their feedback, suggestions, encouragement. Take those two steps now.

Close the session with prayer for some of the specific

needs that surfaced during the sharing.

RECAP: Briefly remind the group that their special prayer focus for the week ahead will be on their work life. Direct them to page 121 of the workbook for the form that will help them organize work-related requests.

ADVANCED PREPARATION FOR LESSON 11: Read the focusing activity for lesson 11 now. Begin to gather and save your junk mail now, and ask group members to do the same.

Lesson 6

ACCOUNTABILITY: During the week preceding this session group members were to focus on work-related requests, making use of the form on page 121 of the workbook. Who are they praying for at work?

FOCUS: Samuel Clemmens was known to be skeptical about most of Christianity's claims. In his novel *The Adventures of Huckleberry Finn*, he has Huck raise the skeptic's challenge to those of us who believe God hears and answers our prayers. Huck says about prayer: "No, there ain't nothin' in it."

Ask: Why are most people skeptical about prayer? What do you believe is the best way to meet this skepticism?

DISCOVER: From the discussion above, move into a review of the four tough questions in the workbook. To cover: "What about apparently senseless suffering?" just give group members an opportunity to share from their own experience how this is a personally relevant question. Ask: "In what ways has this been a very personal (rather than purely intellectual) question for you in your life experience?"

To cover: "Why pray, if God knows what will happen?" go to paragraph two—the one that deals with C.S. Lewis's observation about God granting our prayers from the foundation of time. Ask for reactions to the explanation. Was this a new thought to anyone? Was it helpful? Confusing?

To cover: "Can I really get God to do something?" ask: When have you wished you could *make* God work things out to your liking? Have you always found that your way was best?

To cover: "What about unanswered prayer?" after going over workbook answers, have the group read Matthew 7:9-11 and compare it with Luke 11:11-13. Ask: "What is a major difference between the two passages? (Hint: What words in Luke are parallel to Matthew's "give good gifts"?)

From this exercise, make the point that ultimately, God Himself is the answer to all of our prayers. Human fathers give us many good things, but God gives us His nature!

RESPOND: Use the last few minutes of your session time for group sharing of any lingering intellectual question they still have, or ways the lesson "answers" seemed incomplete or unsatisfying. After prayer, close with a Scripture reading of Isaiah 55:8, 9.

RECAP: Briefly remind group members that during the week ahead they are to prepare a separate prayer list for their own immediate family and relatives. Refer them to page 122 of the workbook.

Lesson 7

ACCOUNTABILITY: During the week leading up to this session group members were to prepare a separate prayer list for their immediate family and relatives. How many were able to do that? Who would like to share any special family prayer concerns that the group could pray about?

FOCUS: Begin by asking: "Who is the greatest or most admired person of prayer you have known? Share about

134

that person." After sharing the names, discuss: 1) Do great examples encourage you or tend to discourage you? Why?

DISCOVER: Go through the first three sections of the lesson, sharing and discussing answers to the workbook questions. Then spend the bulk of your time on the "What Did Jesus Pray?" section, dealing with John 17.

Divide into three groups, assigning one section of John 17 to each (1-5, 6-19, 20-26). Each group should read its assigned section and do three things: 1) make a list of every request of Jesus in that section; 2) for each request, develop a *specific* practical application to our present-day prayer lives; 3) report back to the large group.

Sum up this section by making the point that *intercession* is a prime task of every Christian.

RESPOND: Hebrews 7:24, 25 is a powerful, potentially life changing passage of Scripture—if we could only believe it and live in its power! Let's wrap up this session by helping the truth of these verses (that Jesus intercedes for us) come alive for us with greater impact.

Ask everyone to prepare themselves for a period of silence and meditation. Take a moment for everyone to get comfortable and to relax—perhaps with eyes closed—as you read to them Hebrews 7:24, 25.

After reading, say: "Now, in the next few minutes of silence, meditate on a 'vision' of Jesus praying for you, with all that this truth means for you. Use your imagination to bring that reality to life in your feelings. Let yourself sense, deep inside, the love and care Jesus has for you as He approaches the Father on your behalf. He loves you. He wants the best for you. He prays for you every day. Meditate on this."

After two or three minutes of silence, say: "Now say a brief prayer to Jesus, telling Him what you want Him to put on His prayer list for you. Then I will close in prayer." For your closing prayer, consider use the benediction found in Jude 24, 25.

RECAP: Briefly remind the group that during the week ahead their PMC should provide them with requests that he or she has selected from your denomination or church group headquarters.

Lesson 8

ACCOUNTABILITY: During the week preceding this session group members were to add to their prayer lists denominational requests supplied by the Prayer Ministers Coordinator. Has this been done? How is the PMC handling his or her responsibilities? Any special encouragement required at this point?

FOCUS: Begin by letting someone summarize the contrast that is dealt with in the quote by John Stott in the lesson—the contrast between heathen praying and Christian praying. Ask: What aspect of this contrast gives you the most encouragement when you think about how God wants to relate to you in prayer?

DISCOVER: Now work through the Prayer together, phrase by phrase, using the following discussion questions:

1. How can hallowing God's name fit with conversational prayer?

2. In what ways have you seen God's "kingdom come" in your own life in the past year?

3. Let those who are willing share their answers to questions under "Give Us . . .".This could be a real exercise in mutual encouragement as the group observes how God is already providing daily—with either answered prayer or His grace and peace to weather the problems in His strength.

4. Allow for, but do not to push for sharing of workbook

answers under "Forgive us . . ." unless the group is ready. Consider the "comfort level" of your group in regard to sharing some of the personal issues about forgiving and forgiveness.

5. Focus in on questions 2 and 3 about "making no provision for the flesh." (Again, some may be willing to share their answers—others would rather keep them private. That's okay!)

RESPOND: Spend a brief period of time sharing ideas about how all of you could start using the Lord's Prayer and/or the prayer principles in your daily prayer times. Close by saying (or reading) the Lord's Prayer in unison as your benediction.

RECAP: Briefly remind the group that during the week ahead they should be recieving from the PMC a list of prayer requests for missions—or, if necessary, compling their own list. Refer them to page 123 of the workbook.

Lesson 9

ACCOUNTABILITY: During the week preceding this session group members should have (with the help of the PMC) worked at compiling a list of prayer requests for missions. What special requests do they have to share with the group?

FOCUS: Begin your focus on the theme of learning from others by placing the lead-in phrase from the workbook lesson on the chalkboard (or simply say it): **Example is better than precept.** Say: "Share about a time when you found this to be true in your life." After a time of sharing, say: "This principle can be true in learning to pray, too— at least in part. Let's dig into the lesson and look more closely at some of those Bible pray-ers/prayers and see what we can learn from them . . . ."

DISCOVER: To cover "Enlightening Exercise":

1. List a good number of your group members' "Prayer principles to apply" responses on the chalkboard. That is, summarize one or two personal applications for each pray-er by distilling the comments of everyone. (Note: this will probably be quite an overwhelming list!)

2. Then stand back, take an overall look at the list, and discuss them.

To cover "Enduring Examples":

Have group members divide into groups of two or three. Each group chooses one of the pray-ers to "major" on and prepare a brief (two minute) report on that person by studying the Bible passage given. The groups' report will follow the outline below:

1. This person's overriding view of God:

2. What moved this person to pray:

3. Why the prayer is a good example of how a Christian should pray today:

4. Insights received from the author's comments on this person's experience:

5. The one thing I would like to emulate from this person's life and prayers:

When the small groups have prepared their reports, let them present the material to the larger group.

RESPOND: Give group members a chance to practice interceding for one another using the prayer of Paul (Eph. 3:14-21) as their model. Let them choose a partner, go to a private area in the room or building, and pray this prayer to one another. For example:

I pray for you, Susan, that out of God's glorious riches He may strengthen you . . . . etc.

RECAP: Briefly remind the group that during the week ahead they will be working on prayer requests for government and national concerns. Refer them to page 124 of the workbook.

Lesson 10

ACCOUNTABILITY: During the week preceding this session group members were to work on developing a list of government and national prayer concerns, listing these on page ??? of the workbook. Have they done this? Has the PMC been faithfully supplying grist for the prayer ministry of this group? How is it going?

FOCUS: Have group members work at coming up with their own personal behavioral definitions of "faith." A behavioral definition is one that uses an experience, rather than just descriptive words, to indicate the essence of the word being defined. For example:

"Temptation is getting back $10 too much in change."

"Love is never having to say you're sorry."

"Happiness is striving for a goal."

"Faith is _____."

After sharing your definitions, discuss: "If you had more faith right now, how would your life be different?"

DISCOVER: Read Hebrews 11:1 for the Biblical definition of faith. Then focus on the workbook questions on pages 97 and 98 that ask for specific personal application regarding the place of faith in your group members' lives.

Use the rest of your time for the following activity relating to the "Increasing Your Faith" section. Have a rotating "success story" panel as a means of mutual encouragement. For the panel: ask 3 or 4 volunteers to take turns being a "panel of one." Perhaps each volunteer could move to sit in the "panel chair" when it is his/her turn to be the panel. The volunteer will share one instance in life in which he/she experienced a growth in faith. It does not have to be dramatic; it can be quite commonplace. But it was a growth experience, and could be helpful to others if they could find out about it.

The rest of the group members will have an opportunity to ask questions about this experience to get an idea of the myriad ways God can work in lives. They could ask such questions as:

-How/when did you sense your faith had grown?

-What did you do "right" or "wrong "?

-What part did doubt/fear/anger play in your experience?

-What advice would you have for others going through similar situations?

Leave some time after this exercise for any additional comments about the author's four statements regarding how faith increases.

Respond: Close with a time of prayer in which the group will pray after the manner of the father in Mark 9:24. What concerns do group members have that they need more faith about? Pray together about these things at the level of belief that is present, asking for power to overcome the unbelief that remains.

Recap: Briefly remind the group that during the week ahead they should be thinking about how their group could carry on its prayer ministry after this course is completed. Come to the next session ready to talk this over and share any ideas together.

REMINDER: Bring your "scheming" junk mail to the group session next week.

Lesson 11

Accountability: During the week preceding this session, group members were to think about how their group could carry on its prayer ministry after this course is completed. You will discuss this during the "Response to the Word" section of this lesson.

Focus: You and other group members should have brought "junk mail" to this group session. Pick out pieces that seem particularly "scheming." Share your pieces of mail, and let others do the same, pointing out the tricky parts of the advertising. Then ask: How vulnerable are you to these kinds of schemes? Why? How do you go about withstanding such schemes? In what ways are such schemes like and unlike the schemes of the devil? How do you go about withstanding the devil's schemes in your life?

Make the point that the main way we withstand the devil's schemes is to live in close relationship to the Lord, praying with authority. This lesson looks more closely at what praying with authority means.

DISCOVER: Lead your group through a chart fill-in exercise. In advance, put the chart below on chalkboard or newsprint. Say: "As the workbook points out, praying with authority involves being in the presence and power of the Spirit. But what is that presence and power like?" Have group members fill in the chart, giving their ideas about this from their knowledge of Scripture and from personal experience.

"In the same way, praying with authority means depending on Jesus' authority (i.e., praying "in His name"). In the chart, fill in what Jesus' authority is like.

"Finally, praying with authority means having a sense of what God's will is like and seeking to carry it out. In the chart, fill in some characteristics of God's will as you understand it from Scripture and your own personal experience."

After the left column is filled in, brainstorm with the group about how understanding the characteristics of the Spirit's presence, Christ's authority, and God's will apply to the practice of prayer.

Characteristics   **Prayer Implications**
Characteristics of
the Spirit's presence
and power:
(see John 14—16; Acts 2)

Characteristics of
Jesus' authority:
(see John 8:12-29)

Characteristics of
God's will:
(see Rom. 12:2)

After the whole chart is filled in, discuss:
• In light of this chart, how well are you prepared to pray
with authority?
• What changes in your life/prayers would need to take
place for you to have a sense of praying with more authority?

RESPOND: Use the response time to go through the four
suggestions under the "Your Ministry of Prayer" section.
Solidify your plans for continuing the group's prayer
ministry after the course is completed.

Lesson 12

ACCOUNTABILITY: At the beginning of the class session, take
time to thoroughly review the plans you have been developing for continuing your prayer ministry as a group after
this course is completed. What still needs to be discussed?
What action now needs to be taken? Who will be responsible for what?

FOCUS: Open the class by thinking about situations in
which there was "no one to help." Ask: "Have you ever
been in a situation in which you really needed someone to
come to your aid, but no one did?"
• Share about that situation. What happened?
• How did you feel as you struggled with the problem
alone?
• Can you relate this experience to the spiritual reality of
the lack of intercessors in our world today? Explain.

DISCOVER: Say: Let's read about the age-old need for those

who respond to the call for help—for intercessors. Read Isaiah 59 aloud in two parts: first, verses 1-19, then ask:
• The workbook calls Isaiah 59 a "mirror." What are some specific parallels to modern society that you see in verses 1-19?
• Who are the ones in that day and in ours who must feel "left out in the cold" with no one to help them? How does their plight make you feel?

Then read verses 20, 21. Ask:
• What are some reasons for hopefulness that you see coming through in verses 20, 21?
• In what ways do you view your personal ministry of prayer as a response to God's call for intercessors? Does this feel like a worthy, necessary, important calling? Share.

RESPOND: The needs of your group will largely determine how you will use the response time for this last lesson of the course. So before class, carefully think through what needs to be done during this time to bring the course to significant closure while leading the group to think in terms of ongoing ministry. The LAMP curriculum seeks to launch individuals and groups into ongoing ministry within the church. What can be done during this response time to encourage movement toward that goal?

At the least, you will want to do the following three things during this time:

1. Focus on the three questions under "Time Management for Prayer" and spend some time sharing individual goals for members' personal prayer lives.
2. Discuss group plans for future prayer ministry. Go over the workbook suggestions under "Organizing for Ongoing Ministry" and "Plan 'B'" and discuss which options seem viable for your particular group. *Strongly consider whether the group would like to meet again in the near future for a potluck around which further discussion could take place.*
3. Spend time affirming one another and celebrating the accomplishments of the group.

143